MYTHS AND LEGENDS OF IRELAND

A Celtic Journey Through an Ancient and Enchanted Land

EITHNE MASSEY

FALL RIVER PRESS

Originally published as *Legendary Ireland*

This 2008 edition published by Fall River Press by arrangement with
The O'Brien Press, Ltd.

See page 5 for photo credits.

ISBN-13: 978-1-4351-0467-9
ISBN-10: 1-4351-0467-6

Printed and bound in China

10 9 8 7 6 5 4 3 2 1

This book is for my parents, William and Eileen Massey

Acknowledgments

The author would like to thank the Head of the Department of Irish Folklore, University College Dublin for permission to use material from IFC S 575: 172–356 in the section on Lough Muskry. Thanks are due also to the staff of the Department, the staff of the National Library, UCD Library and Dublin City Library Service for their assistance during the research for this project. The staff at O'Brien Press and, in particular, Susan Houlden have my gratitude for their support during the making of Myths and Legends of Ireland.

I would like to thank the following people for their hospitality: Frances Crickard and Davy and Leon McGovan in Antrim; the Murphy family in Cork; the Poole family in Donegal; and Maureen Massey and Johnnie Doyle in Kerry. Thanks are also due to those who accompanied us on various site visits: Maura Leahy, Catherine Groves, Conall Mac Riocard, and Maureen, William and Donal Massey. I would also like to thank all those unknown people who assisted us on our travels during the past year. We encountered nothing but kindness from Tory Island to Béara. A special thank you is due to Michael Lavelle, and Michael James Gaughan and crew, for getting us to Inis Glora when we thought the cause was lost.

Finally, I would like to thank my sister Fidelma Massey for her perceptive comments on the introduction, and indeed all my family and friends, who helped us out with everything from advice and encouragement to dog-minding during the time this book was written.

Photo Credits

The author and publisher would like to thank the following for permission to reproduce photographs: Dúchas The Heritage Service: p55; The Irish Image Collection: p22,46,134,175,185; Jacques Le Goff: p2 (author and self photographs), 18, 84, 99, 112, 139, 146, 158, 191, 197, 203, 211; Peter Mulryan: p39; Pip Sides: p1, 2–3 (background and self photographs), 6–7, 8, 31, 34, 62, 68, 77, 79, 91, 92–3, 105, 119, 126, 152, 169, 218.

The engravings reproduced in this book were taken from Hall's Ireland Vols I–III *and* Grose's Antiquities, Vols I and II. *The author and publisher have endeavoured to establish the origin of all images used, and they apologise if any name has been omitted.*

Contents

Acknowledgments 5
Introduction 9

LEINSTER

Howth Head, Dublin 19
Bécuma of the Fair Skin 21

Ardee, Louth 28
The Fight at the Ford 30

Cooley, Louth 36
The Battle of the Bulls 38

Tara, Meath 42
The Magic Branch 45

Newgrange and the Boyne Valley, Meath 50
The Revenge of Sín 55

Hill of Uisneach, Westmeath 59
Fintan the Seer 61

Glencree, Wicklow 64
Da Dearga's Hostel 66

St. Mullins, Carlow 72
The Death of Suibhne 74

MUNSTER

Lough Muskry, Tipperary 82
The Vision of Aonghus 84

Slievenamon, Tipperary 87
The Birth of Oisín 89

Béara Peninsula, Cork 95
The Hag of Béara 97

Killarney, Kerry 101
The Return of Oisín 104

Caherconree, Kerry 108
The Death of Cú Roí 111

Knockainey, Limerick 116
Áine of Knockainey 118

Doonbeg, Clare 122
Donn, Lord of the Red Palace 125

CONNACHT

Dún Aonghusa, the Aran Islands, Galway 130

The Last of the Fir Bolg 133

Lough Corrib, Galway 136

Manannán and the Crane Bag 139

Inis Glora and the Erris Peninsula, Mayo 141

The Children of Lir 144

Rathcroghan, Roscommon 149

Pillow Talk: The Beginning of the *Táin Bó Cuailgne* 153

Ardagh Hill, Longford 157

The Finding of Étaín 160

Keshcorann Caves, Sligo 165

The Hags of Winter 167

Ben Bulben, Sligo 171

The Story of Diarmaid and Gráinne 174

ULSTER

Grianán of Aileach, Donegal 182

The Gods of the Hill 184

Tory Island, Donegal 187

The Birth of Lugh 190

Lough Neagh, Tyrone 194

Lí Ban the Mermaid 196

Ballycastle, Antrim 200

The Tragedy of Deirdre 202

Giant's Causeway, Antrim 207

Fionn's Visitor 210

Emain Macha, Armagh 213

Macha's Curse 216

Time Chart 221

Glossary of Main Characters 222

Glossary of Archaeological Terms 230

Map of Sites 233

Direction Key 234

Bibliography 237

Introduction

Ireland is an island of stories, some of which stretch back over many centuries and have their roots in a tradition that goes back even further. Many of these legends have close associations with particular places. This book retells just some of these legends and links them with the places from which they grew. Place and story are inextricably bound together, and so in the arrangement of the stories I have followed a geographical sequence rather than the traditional division into four cycles.

However, these traditional divisions do provide a useful context in which to gain a sense of the richness of the world of the Celtic legends. The first of these, the Mythological Cycle, tells the tale of the very origins of human life in Ireland. The stories deal with the successive invasions of the island, the great battles between the tribes of the Tuatha Dé Danann (the divine people of the goddess Danu) and the Fomorians, the demonic tribe who competed with them for control of Ireland. They also include the stories of the Sídh (those mythical beings which share human passions but not human sickness and age), such as that of the lovers Midhir and Étaín. The second cycle is the Ulster Cycle, which has at its heart the great epic of the *Táin Bó Cuailgne,* (*The Cattle Raid of Cooley*). The central story of the battle between Conchobhar, king of Ulster, and Maeve, queen of Connacht, encompasses the exploits of the great hero, Cú Chulainn. This cycle includes associated stories such as that of Deirdre. There has been much dispute between scholars about the period in which the Ulster Cycle is set. Conchobhar, King of Ulster, was said to have lived in the first century AD, and the nature of the society portrayed—warrior-like and tribal—seems close to our perceptions of the Celtic Iron Age. But Maeve, for example, has her roots as a goddess figure much further back in time, as do many of the figures woven into the tapestry of the stories. Similar uncertainty surrounds the stories of the Fianna Cycle. These stories deal with Fionn and his hunter companions, including the epic pursuit of Diarmuid and

Opposite:
Statue of Cú Chulainn carrying the dead Ferdia, Ardee, County Louth.

Gráinne. The Fianna Cycle stories take place in the natural world rather than in the courts of the kings, and the "fian" actually existed as a group of young warriors who lived in small groups outside society. The stories are set at the time of Cormac Mac Airt, who was said to have reigned as high king in the third century AD, but the genesis of the figure of Fionn is probably far older than this. The fourth cycle, known as the Historical Cycle or the Cycle of the Kings, has its stories set in a later period, and some of the characters involved are based on actual historical characters living in a Christian society. However, here, as in all the legends, different worlds and different periods intertwine and historical characters drift in and out of the landscape of legend. It is impossible to establish a clear and consistent chronology, all the more so as the stories were written down many centuries after they had already had a long history as part of an oral tradition. This oral tradition indicates that while extant texts date from no earlier than the eleventh and twelfth centuries, many of the stories were originally written down up to four centuries earlier. The Ulster Cycle tales may have been written down as early as the seventh century and they portray a world that is undeniably pre-Christian in its ethos. Irish literature is the earliest vernacular literature in western Europe and, while scholars have argued over the historical existence of its heroes, and queens and kings, whatever human existence these characters may have had has long been concealed under the layers of a thousand re-tellings. I therefore make no apologies for telling these stories once again in contemporary language, or for the slight liberties I have taken with some of the texts. Every society retells its myths in a slightly different form and the texts we have of the tales are the products of a medieval Christian society where the stories were recorded by clerics who added their own gloss to the versions they wrote.

Having said this, I must add that the amount of loving effort the scribes put into producing and preserving these beautiful manuscripts indicates how important these stories were to their society. And through all their re-tellings the stories retain a distinctive sense of the sacredness of the natural, sensual world; they celebrate it in its entirety, from the joy of the blackbird's song in spring to the cold beauty of winter. St. Colmcille is said to have been more frightened by the sound of the axe in his beloved oak grove at Derry than of death and hell, and early Irish lyrics, many written by monks, include many lovely celebrations of the natural world. This close connection with the natural world and with the features of the landscape is also found in the poems of the *Dindshenchas*, the lore of places, which gives us the stories associated with the names of particular places and is a major source for Irish legends. Other important sources are the *Leabhar Gabhála Éireann*—commonly known as *The Book of Invasions*, and the *Leabhar Laighean—The Book of Leinster*, both compiled in the twelfth century, together with the *Leabhar na hUidhre* or *The Book of the Dun Cow* which is late eleventh or very early twelfth century. The original texts are inaccessible to all but Gaelic scholars but it is worth looking at some of the translations to get a sense of the complexity and beauty of the original language.

Although one might hope to be on firmer ground when dealing with the physical places and the man-made structures associated with the stories, in reality the situation is almost as confusing. Structures such as burial chambers and earthen mounds have been neatly classified by archaeologists, but as in the stories, scholarship can classify but cannot fully explain. Some of the sites visited in this book show evidence of settlement as far back as 5,000 years ago, dating from the New Stone Age or Neolithic period; while in other cases the structures are as late as the tenth century. A great many of the sites show evidence of layer upon layer of settlement, and in many cases there is no consensus as to what their purpose was. The only generalisations that can be made are that many of the structures mentioned in the book were used as tombs of one kind or another, or at least show evidence that burials were carried out there, while others seem to be places where the community gathered for defence or celebration.

The categories used by archaeologists divide the period of prehistory into various time spans. These divisions are based on cultural change rather than strictly on timescale, and sometimes vary from place to place—for example, one community might still be living a Neolithic (i.e. New Stone Age) existence while another nearby might be using bronze and have developed corresponding social structures.

Human occupation in Ireland dates from 9,000 years ago when people lived by hunting, fishing and gathering wild plants. This way of life was fairly widespread over Ireland at sites such as Mount Sandel, County Derry and Ballyferriter, County Kerry. The hunter-gatherers left no traces of field monuments although a controversial date from a passage-grave in Carrowmore in Sligo suggests that they may have begun to build monuments for their dead by the end of the Mesolithic period.

It was the people of the Neolithic period who left their mark on the early landscape, as they settled down to till the land and rear cattle. The great walled fields in north Mayo known as the Céide Fields indicate how they organised their land and how important stock-rearing was to their society. They honoured their ancestors and the dead, and some of the most spectacular Megalithic tombs in Europe are the work of the early farming community in Ireland. There are about 1,450 of these monuments, and many of them became the focus of the lore of places and of the stories which are the subjects of this book. The most famous of them are at the Bend of the Boyne (*Brú na Bóinne*), now a UNESCO World Heritage site with the greatest collection of Neolithic art in Europe. The great cult centre at Tara, County Meath, also has its origins in Neolithic times and has continued for millennia to be a sacred place and a setting for stories of gods and kings. The hundreds of portal dolmens which dot the landscape and are often known locally as *Leaba Dhiarmada agus Gráinne*, are another legacy of the Stone Age builders.

The Bronze Age from *c.*2000BC brought to Ireland's society the use of metal and the beginnings of trade. This was a warlike society, but also a very creative one, which crafted exquisite weapons and jewellery in gold and bronze. Such wealth needs to be defended, so structures such as the great hill-forts began to be built—Dún Aonghusa on the Aran Islands had its beginnings in this period. Standing stones and stone circles were ritual sites for these Bronze Age people and the first *crannógs*, or defensive lake-dwellings were built.

Around 300BC the first Celts arrived in Ireland and ushered in the Iron Age. Hillforts continued to be built and the coast was fringed with defensive promontory forts. Royal sites which also served as great cult and tribal centres were built and are still impressive today. These are at Tara in County Meath, Rathcroghan in County Roscommon, Dún Ailinne in County Kildare and Emhain Macha in County Armagh. They are the buildings of an aristocratic, tribal and violent society which has clear connections with the world portrayed in the *Táin*. This society is one where certain values are held in common; particularly courage, strength, generosity and faithfulness to one's companions and to one's tribe. It is a multi-theistic society, where heroes swear by the gods their people swear by. It is one where music, poetry and rich colours were held in high regard, as were feasting, fighting, racing, hunting and hospitality. In general, however, the attempts that have been made to match the evidence of archaeology or actual historical events with the accounts of the history of Ireland in the *Leabhar Gabhála* or the *Táin* have met with little success. There are no clear patterns and neat correspondences; rather, the world of the stories is a world that is larger inside than it is outside, and where time may be circular as well as linear, possessing the shape-shifting, mutable qualities of the Sídh.

Because of this, a mental shift is needed to enter fully the world of the legends. The stories are the myths created by people—many people over a very long time—from their history and geography, from time and place. Myths have been described as the dreams of the tribe and, like dreams, they take what happens in time—history—and transfigure it. In this world, events may be inconsistent, even contradictory. Because they do not fit into a rational world view, in the light of day their importance can be denied. However, to live without myth is to live without the healing power of dreams and the imagination.

At the same time, the raw material on which the imagination works is rooted in time, in a specific place and in the physical features of the landscape. In the stories, this natural world merges with the world of the collective imagination. So, the emotional power of the stories adds resonance to our encounters with place, and place itself can embody a story in a similar way to that in which the ancient Irish could see a hill as a goddess, or a lake as the embodiment of a god. The word *sídh* can thus mean both a magical being and the mound in the earth where that being lives. A further shift in perception is needed to accept that the same member of the Sídh can have his or her home in many different places—the guardian spirits are very local ones. Many of the people of Ireland, well into the twentieth century, believed that certain trees and wells and hills were under the guardianship of their local otherworld being and each of these enchanted places was protected accordingly. There was an element of fear as well as awe in this relationship, for at certain times, notably at Samhain (Halloween) and Bealtaine (May Eve), you could slip easily from one world into the other.

This feeling of respect for the natural landscape and the ancient remains it holds is under threat. W.B. Yeats once said that "places may begin to seem the only hieroglyphics that cannot be forgotten," but in present-day Ireland, the letters are being erased from the landscape. Driving through Ireland during the first two years of the new millennium, there were times when it felt as if the entire countryside had been placed under siege—home-made posters

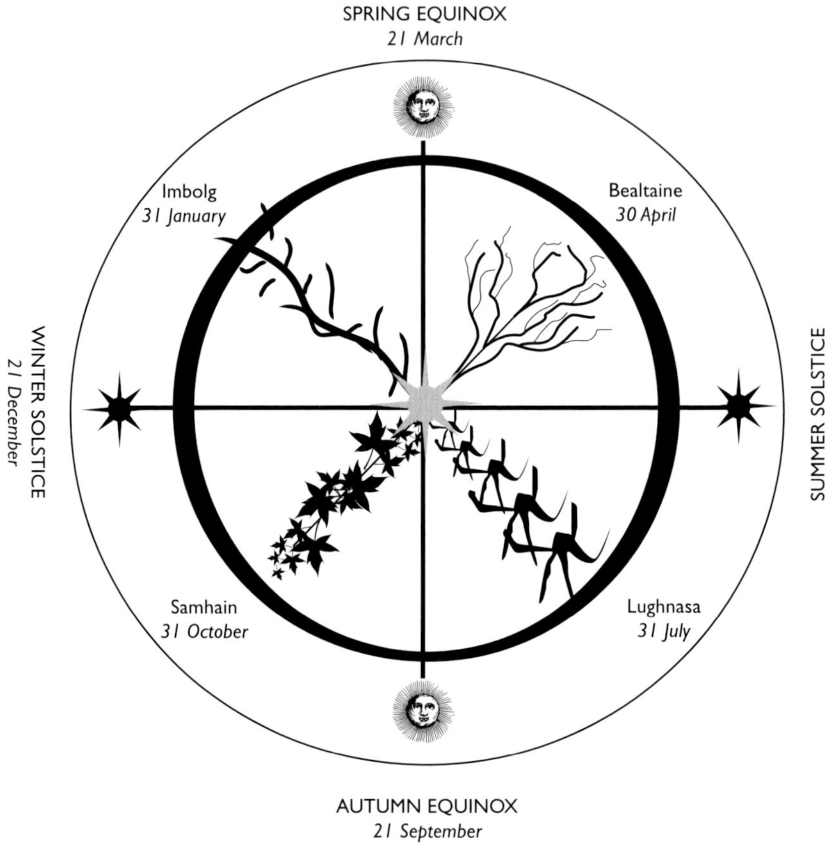

Above: *Celtic wheel of the year.*

protested against plans for super-dumps, or satellite masts on historic hills, or road-widening schemes set to destroy ancient sites. Nor was all the violence against the landscape on the part of outsiders; land improvement is a particular threat to earthen monuments such as raths, and we saw more than one beautiful place hosting its own private super-dump with its antiquities defaced by mindless vandalism. In some cases too, attempts to "develop" a site as a tourist attraction had in fact damaged it beyond repair. There is a definite irony in encouraging people to visit sites which at present owe much of their appeal to the fact that they are largely unvisited. However, unless there is a deep communal appreciation of the worth of the places in this book, we can no longer afford the luxury of assuming that they will resist destruction. Recent reports indicate that, in spite of the legislation introduced to protect these monuments, the rate of their destruction is increasing rather than decreasing. In order for these places to survive, those with power over the landscape—whether they are local landowners or government departments—need to become guardians as well as exploiters, and this relationship needs to be supported by the whole community. There is a Greek myth about a character called Erysicthon, the Earth-Tearer. Erysicthon cut down a grove of sacred trees in order to build his banqueting hall. Demeter, goddess of the fertile fields, at first warned him gently against this sacrilege, but when he threatened her with his axe, she cursed him. He became eternally hungry, and never satisfied. In his greed, he ate filth and became thinner and thinner, hungrier and hungrier, poisoned by his own waste.

The hunger that we feel at this loss of contact with the natural world and its ancient stories is not a physical one, but a kind of spiritual and emotional starvation. Yet feeding this hunger may involve nothing more difficult than walking out into the landscape and looking at it with the eye of the imagination. The power of the human capacity to imagine, to see beyond, reaches us through century after century, and draws us again and again into the indivisible trinity of story, place and people. A landscape will survive as long as there are people to love it, and a story is never quite over as long as there are people to tell it.

When the Sons of Míl, one of the early peoples of Ireland, came to its shores, they asked their poet Amairgen to quiet the waves which were preventing them from landing. The poem with which he did this is an invocation of Ireland:

I invoke the land of Ireland:
Much-coursed be the fertile sea,
Fertile be the fruit-strewn mountain,
Fruit-strewn be the showery wood,
Showery be the river of waterfalls,
Of waterfalls be the lake of deep pools,
Deep-pooled be the hill-top well,
A well of tribes be the assembly,
An assembly of kings be Tara,
Tara be the hill of the tribes,
The tribes of the sons of Míl,
Of Míl the ships, the barks,

Let the lofty bark be Ireland,
Lofty Ireland, darkly sung …
I invoke the land of Ireland.

—"Cross and Slover," ***Ancient Irish Tales***

Leinster

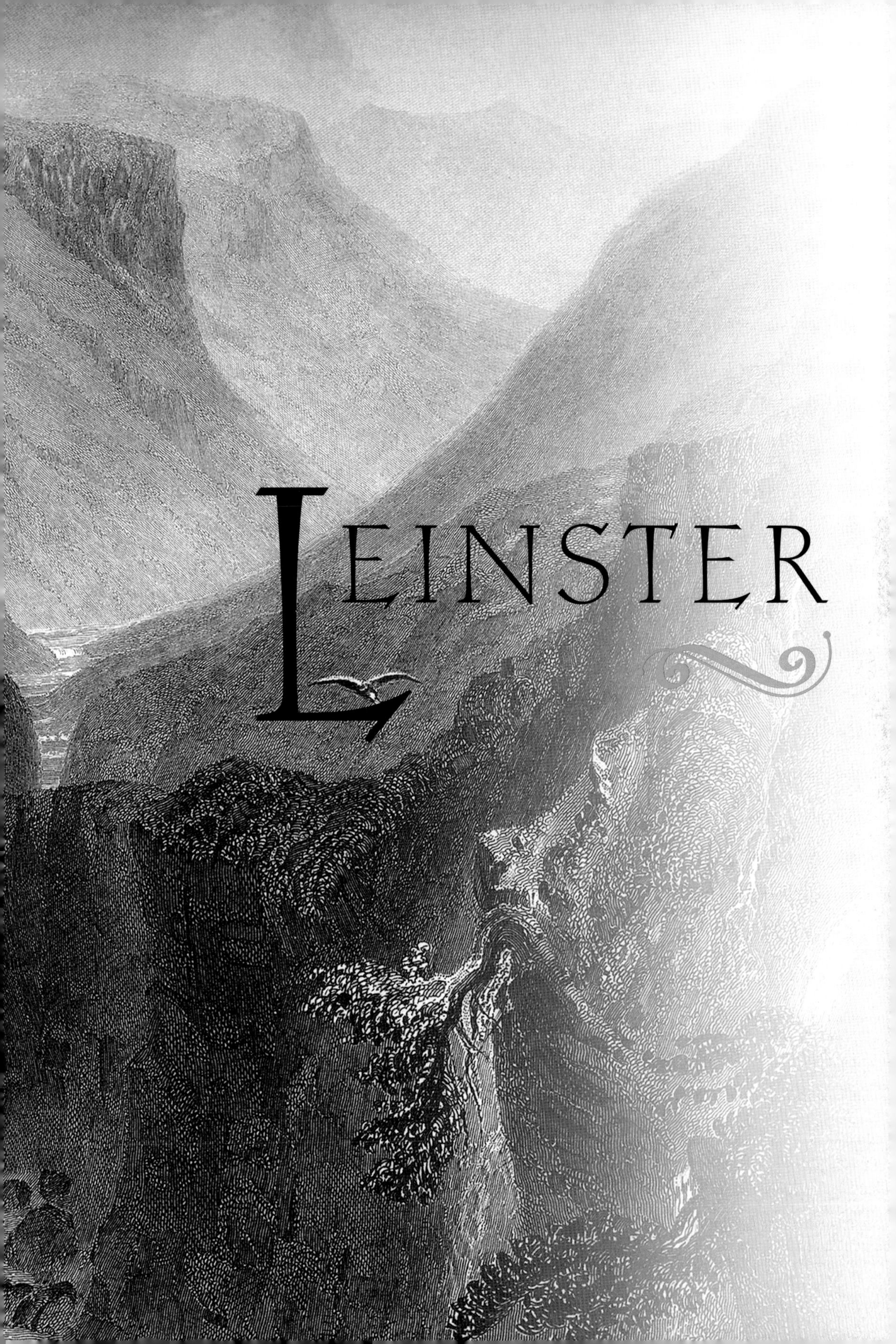

Howth Head, Dublin

BEANN ÉADAIR

Despite its proximity to Dublin, Howth Head retains its sense of being a place apart, particularly if you choose the time of your visit carefully. The best time to visit Howth is on a weekday when the weather is dull and the place is not full of crowds of people trying to get away from the city. This rocky peninsula, once an island, is steeped in history and legend. The original name for the peninsula, *Beann Éadair,* "the Peak of Étar," is said to come from the name of the great warrior, Étar, who died for the love of Áine, the goddess of Knockainey. Diarmaid and Gráinne came here, fleeing from Fionn, and Deirdre and the sons of Usna rested here during their flight from the jealous king Conchobhar.

Howth is an attractive village and the harbour still functions as a fishing port, although these days you are more likely to meet a golfer than a fisherman as you

Pages 16-17:
W.H. Bartlett's nineteenth-century engraving depicting the "Head of Glenmalure," County Wicklow.
Opposite:
Aideen's tomb, a portal tomb in the grounds of Howth Castle.

make your way through its streets. However, to find the real Howth, leave the manicured lawns and expensive restaurants behind you and take one of the many walks by the cliffs or up into the rocky hills. The sites mentioned here are only focal points for a district which has the potential for hours of exploration.

One major site is that of Aideen's Tomb. This is a portal tomb, situated in the grounds of Howth Castle, the traditional home of the St. Lawrence family and now the site of the Deerpark Hotel. The tomb is in the forested area to the right of the hotel and easily accessible from the edge of the golf course. This wilderness is particularly beautiful during late May and early June when the rhododendrons and azaleas are in bloom. The forest on the hilly land behind is worth a visit in its own right, and those who do not mind a scramble can follow a trail to the top of the hills; from the top there are magnificent views. Tradition has it that there is a cave on the hill where Diarmuid and Gráinne slept during their travels.

The tomb itself is a huge structure, partially collapsed, with one of the largest capstones in Ireland, estimated to weigh 90 tonnes (1,771 hundredweight). Portal tombs in Ireland are among the very earliest of Megalithic remains, many dating from before 3000BC. Twisted trees and ferns grow around the tomb, lichen covers the stones, and children climb through it, fascinated by something at once so obviously man-made and at the same time on a scale massive enough to seem the work of giants. Legend tells us that Aideen, or Étaín Fholtfhinn, was a beautiful princess of the Sídh, a famous runner who was also the lover and later the wife of Oscar, grandson of Fionn. When Oscar was killed in battle, Aideen died from grief at his loss. Her home had been the *sídh* of Beann Éadair, and this was where she was taken to be buried. Other traditions state that this was the tomb of Crimthan, a king of the first century AD, and others still that the tomb is that of Étar himself. Whatever the truth of the legends, the tomb in the forest remains a potent, if silent, guardian of Howth's mysterious past.

Howth was a place of many battles, and the promontory fort of Dún Griffin, (also traditionally associated with Crimthan) which surrounds the Baily Lighthouse, shows how important this site was as a defence against invasion. It is generally accepted that such forts, found all around the coast of Ireland, were built for defence against invasion by sea. They may also have been used as ceremonial centres for the gathering of the tribes for fairs or religious purposes. To reach the fort, take the trail leading down from the left of the car park on the summit. Within moments you will see the lighthouse below you. The trail leads through gorse and brambles, ferns and heather, and in early summer it is full of wild garlic. It goes down steeply to the small promontory where the lighthouse stands. Although there is no entry allowed to the grounds of the lighthouse and it is not easy to distinguish the original ditches and ramparts of the fort, it is obvious that this was an ideal defensive site. Sea and high cliffs surround it on three sides, and on the fourth, a narrow neck of rock connects it to the land. To the south is Dublin Bay and the mountains; to the north and east, nothing but sea.

Find a sheltered spot and look down steep slopes covered in sea-pinks to the twisted rocks and green water. There will be no sound but the waves lapping on the pale grey shingle far below, and the cry of the sea birds. The hectic city of Dublin will seem like another world.

Howth is a place of both escape and defence, of the beginning of exile and of coming home, and many of the tales associated with it mirror these themes of the journey outwards and the return. Imagine the warriors watching here, guarding their people from attack from the unknown lands beyond the horizon. Or think of a solitary king who once stood here, listening to the birds crying and watching in astonishment as a figure came towards him over the sea, bringing death and famine in her wake…

Below:
The Baily Lighthouse, Howth Head.

BÉCUMA OF THE FAIR SKIN

The High King of Ireland, Conn of the Hundred Battles, stood on a pebbly beach at Beann Éadair, and looked to the sea for comfort. It was a bright morning and the waves danced onto the seashore, but Conn was as weary and heartsick as it is possible for a man to be. For despite his wealth, his power, and all his prowess in battle, and the great prosperity and peace that had come to the land under his rulership, he had been unable to defeat the greatest enemy of all. Death had come and taken his beloved wife, Eithne, away, and without her he felt lost

and dejected, a man wandering in a mist. He had left the feasts of Tara and had come to be alone with his thoughts, looking out over the sea where his son, Connla, had been taken away by a beautiful woman of the Sídh many years before. At the time, he had wept, but his wife had consoled him, saying: "Yes, it is hard to lose a child to the land of the Sídh; but look you, we have yet one son, Art the Lone One, who is as clever and brave and good as ever a child could be, and likely to be a great king when you and I are gone."

However, now that his wife too had left him, Conn found no comfort in his son's company. Art reminded him too much that strength was with youth and that he himself was no longer young; that there were to be no more great battles and marvellous adventures in love and war. His skills now were those of an old man—diplomacy and wiliness. Conn looked eastwards into the rising sun, as if it could bring him salvation with the daybreak. He thought of his wife's wise words and of her even temper that had saved him from many a hasty action; and he thought, most painfully of all, of her arms around him in their bed, and her small feet wrapping themselves around his legs for warmth during the cold nights of winter. The king blinked through his tears and rubbed his eyes. Coming towards him over the silver waves was a coracle, a coracle that seemed to move without oar or sail, and standing in it was a figure that glowed in the light of dawn. As it came nearer, Conn realised that it was the most beautiful woman he had ever seen.

Bécuma of the Sídh, she of the Fair Skin, smiled her secret smile as she watched the figure on the shore shade his eyes with his hand to watch her approach. She knew who he was, and although she found his son, Art, more to her liking, she had decided that she was in no position to be choosy. She would start with the father and, in time, no doubt the son would come to her. Bécuma had never left herself in want of anything, which was why she had been banished from the Many-Coloured Land; she had betrayed her husband and the choice had been death by fire or banishment to the mortal realm. She had chosen banishment, but her people had warned her not to attempt to enter any of the *sídh* of Ireland, for their doors were closed against her. Her silver coracle brought her to land, and she heard Conn's gasp as she stepped onto the shore, lifting her red satin cloak and grass-green gown out of the water as she did so. Her hair was yellow-gold, her eyes a clear grey, her skin like the first snow of winter. Now she was close enough for him to smell her perfume, which seemed to Conn like the scent of whitethorn on a warm summer's day. He opened his mouth to ask her who she was, but before the words were out of his mouth, she

Left:
Howth Head and Dublin Bay.

said: "I am Dealbhchaem. The fame of your son Art has spread to the Many-Coloured Land and I have come to seek his love."

Conn frowned. "You wish to marry my son then? Indeed, that is not good news to me."

"Who shall I marry then?" she asked softly.

"Why, none but myself," said Conn.

Bécuma bowed her head and put her hand in his.

"If it is your wish, so it shall be," she said. "But grant me something in return. It would not be right to have Art at Tara so soon after we are wed, for I would wish to forget him. Send him away for a year."

The king was perturbed. "I would not wish to banish my own son for no reason," he said.

Bécuma sighed and raised innocent grey eyes to the king's. Conn paused. Perhaps the maiden was right; his son, so young and strong, might not be a good person to have around them so soon after their marriage.

"It could hurt him to see you in the place of his mother," he said thoughtfully. "I will do as you wish."

The pair travelled to Tara; there, Conn made the order to send his son from the kingdom, not even stopping to bid him farewell. For the first few months, he was deliriously happy with his beautiful young wife. Every day, Bécuma charmed him further. So enchanted was he that at first he did not notice how badly things were going with the land of Ireland. The cows gave no milk, the corn did not grow, the bees made no honey. Blight fell on all of nature so that even the women bore no children and the people began to murmur that there was a curse on the land. The poets and magicians met together and by their arts discovered that their new queen was not, in fact, Dealbhchaem, but Bécuma who had been banished from the Many-Coloured Land for her misdeeds; they told the king that he must send her away.

"I do not care if her name is Dealbhchaem or Bécuma or the Morrigan itself," said Conn. "She is my beloved wife and I will not send her away. Find another way to rid the land of this blight."

So the magicians conferred again, and they came back to the king with the news that if the son of a sinless couple could be found, and his blood mixed with the soil of Tara, the land would be made fertile again. Conn said that he would go on a quest to seek the sinless one. His magicians told him that it might be better to send his son, Art. But Conn had grown so tired of looking at the sad faces and listening to the hungry, crying children who surrounded him that he said angrily: "No—it is my task to save the land." He went to Beann Éadair, where he found Bécuma's coracle and went away over the sea. He left the rule of Ireland under the stewardship of Art.

Conn returned, after many months, with a young boy from a magic island; Segda was the child of a sinless couple and the king had tricked him into coming with him back to Ireland, planning to murder him so that the land might prosper once again. However, there was much dissension that a sinless child should suffer for the fault of the king, and, at the last moment, Segda was rescued by his mother, a woman of the Sídh. She appeared before the king and the nobles and said, "I tell you that it will make no difference whether you kill the boy or not; your evils will not leave you until the cause of evil herself has left."

At this, the old woman fixed a steely eye on Bécuma, so lovely in her green robe and red-golden crown.

"As long as Bécuma stays in the land, it will have no luck."

Then she took Segda's hand and they both disappeared.

Ireland continued to suffer, and Conn, though he still was enslaved by Bécuma, grew greyer and more disconsolate. Meanwhile, Bécuma thought more and more of how handsome his son was in comparison, and how nobly he had ruled the land during his father's absence, so that she began to seek him out, to ask him to ride with her, to sing with her, to play chess. However, Art avoided her all he could, and when he looked at her there was nothing but coldness in his eyes, for he saw her as the blight of the land and the destroyer of his father's honour. Things went on thus until, one day, Bécuma came upon Art playing chess with Cromdes the Magician on the lawn before Tara. She demanded a game with Art, for stakes to be chosen after the match. Then she deliberately lost the first game. As a prize, Art demanded from her the wand of the great magician, Cú Roí. With the help of her foster sister, Áine, Bécuma managed to get the wand. When she brought it to Art, she asked, "Are you impressed, then, with my power?" but he said nothing.

So Bécuma said, "Well then, sulky boy, I demand a return game."

Art had no choice but to agree, and, as they played, Áine of the Sídh moved one of his pieces so that he lost.

"I did not move that piece," he said angrily.

"Nor did I," said Bécuma, still smiling her secret smile. "But now I have won, and my task for you, as the loser, is to find Dealbhchaem, daughter of Morgan, and bring her back to Tara."

"Where is she?" asked Art.

"She is to the west," said Bécuma.

As Art took a coracle out from Inver Colpa, the Boyne estuary, Bécuma watched him, sure that he would never come back. When Conn heard that Art had left Tara to seek the giant Morgan, he went to his room and stayed there. He did not speak to Bécuma and Bécuma did not come to speak to him, and all around them, the land of Ireland turned to grey ash.

Art travelled for a long time, staying for some time with a woman of the Sídh, Crede, who loved him and wished to keep him with her on her island, but Art had promised to return with Dealbhchaem and rout Bécuma from Tara. So, Crede decided that she would help Art to rescue Dealbhchaem, for she said, "Even if you do not wish to stay with me, I do not want you to finish with your head stuck on a picket outside Morgan's house, like the others who have tried to save the princess."

Crede told Art that Dealbhchaem's mother, the Dog Head, would try her best to kill him even before Morgan discovered that he was there, as it was fated that she would die the day her daughter was wed. She advised him on how to defeat Morgan and sent him on his way, watching him as he sailed out of sight beyond the blue horizon, and fearful that he was leaving her to meet his death.

No sooner had Crede's island disappeared out of Art's sight than the sea became rough and the wind began to howl, and out of the depths great sea-monsters raised their heads, ready to attack him, but Art fought them off. When at last he came to land, it was a place no more comforting than the sea that he had left behind him. Here he had to make his way through a dark, dense forest where the thorns seemed to jump out to bite his flesh. In the forest, he was attacked by seven hags who wanted to bury him in a bath of molten lead; he killed them and left them lying in that same bath. After the forest came a mountain of ice where he almost froze to death; and he had no sooner reached its base than he found himself in a glen, full of giant toads which spat venom at him. He slew the toads, and the giant Ailill of the Black Teeth and the lions who guarded the way to Morgan's *dún*. Finally he reached the *dún*, and there, on a high pillar, was Dealbhchaem, imprisoned in a tiny glass chamber. When he saw her looking out at him, Art realised that all the dangers he had passed through had been worthwhile, for here was a girl even more beautiful than Bécuma, and without the knowing, mocking eyes of that lady. Two girls approached Art and offered him a drink, but he remembered Crede's warning and drank only from the right-hand cup, for Crede had told him that the left-hand one was poison. Then, Dog Head came out, in her armour and ready for the fight—and a horrible sight she was, for she had the head of a wicked black dog. It was a savage battle, but finally Art prevailed and he placed Dog Head's own head on a spike of the palings of the *dún*. There was a crashing of the trees and a roaring in the forest and the giant Morgan approached; Art made himself ready for battle again. As the pair fought, they shifted shape so many times that the creatures of the place looked on in amazement and Dealbhchaem could hardly bear to look at all. As the sun began to set and it seemed to all who looked on that the battle could continue no longer, Art raised his sword and with a great blow chopped the head from the giant's shoulders and let it join his wife's on the palings. He stood at the bottom of the tower and smiled up at Dealbhchaem. When he begged her to come and be his queen in Ireland, this was very much to her taste, for she was tired of being imprisoned in her glass tower.

When they returned to Tara, it was sunset. Where Dealbhchaem walked, the grass sprang up green under her feet, and small birds sang around her head, as if she herself was the spring come again to the land. They could see Bécuma standing on the ramparts, her face a study in rage and fear, for she had never expected Art to return. In the red glow of the evening sun, her beauty seemed somehow distorted. And Dealbhchaem put her hand gently on Art's arm to prevent him from going forward. Instead, she herself went up to Bécuma and said, "Get you hence, you who have made Ireland a wasteland. A new king comes to take up power, and a new queen, and your day is done here. We care not where you go, for every *sídh* in Ireland is closed to you, and you may never return to the Many-Coloured Land; but wherever you go, let it be far away from us and from all of Ireland."

Bécuma said nothing. She turned and walked out of the portals of Tara, dressed in the green gown and red cloak that she had worn the day she came to Beann Éadair. She walked proudly into the darkness that was falling over the land of Ireland, and never once looked back.

Ardee, Louth

BAILE ÁTH FHIRDIA

The eye of faith is needed to appreciate the connection of Ardee with one of the most moving stories of the *Táin Bó Cuailgne* (*The Cattle Raid of Cooley*), the great epic of the Celtic Iron Age. The tale tells of the efforts of Maeve, queen of Connacht, to gain possession of the Brown Bull of Cooley. Great battles were fought and many heroes died, but at Ardee there is not much to see of the old heroic days, apart from the small River Dee and a few stones marking a ford. However, as the poet Patrick Kavanagh said when he talked of the hills around his home, "gods make their own importance," and so too do heroes. Ardee lies at the centre of Muirtheimhne, the territory of Cú Chulainn's birth and one that played an important part in the power struggles of the Iron Age.

Above:
Ardee Castle, County Louth.

The stream flowing on the outskirts of this comfortable and prosperous town was once the site of the epic battle between Cú Chulainn and his foster brother, the great hero of Connacht, Ferdia, who is commemorated in the town's name, *Baile Áth Fhirdia*, "The Town of Ferdia's Ford."

It marked one of the boundaries of Ulster—a province cut off from the counties to the south by bogs and mountains—and for many centuries was one of the heartlands of the Gaelic tribes. By the reign of Elizabeth I, Ulster was a separate, impenetrable area, almost immune to the English monarch's control. By this time, however, the town of Ardee had become a town of the Pale—a community which existed well within the borders of English control. The walls, gates and castles of the new settlers had replaced whatever settlement had been there in pre-Norman times.

The county of Louth has preserved much of its medieval heritage, and the castle in Ardee, built in the thirteenth century by Robert de Pippart, has recently been restored. Both James II and William of Orange lodged at the castle on their way to the momentous Battle of the Boyne in 1690.

The ford is easily reached by following the left bank of the river from the Dublin side of the bridge on the N2. Close one eye to block out the modern houses and factories and try to hear the noise of the battle above the roar of traffic going through the town—not an easy task. To be fair to the good people of Ardee, a park has been made on the banks of the river and the fine stone bridge has been carefully preserved, unlike many Irish towns where the demands of traffic have been put before respect for such venerable structures. On the banks of the river, the people of Ardee have even erected a statue of the two heroes of the combat, with Cú Chulainn holding Ferdia in his arms as he sings his lament for his dead companion.

Ardee is also a good central point for touring Louth and neighbouring Meath, including the Boyne Valley complex. Within easy distance lies the village of Slane, with its dramatic approach from the south and its magnificent castle. Other small towns and villages in the vicinity, such as Castlebellingham, demonstrate a palpable sense of pride in their past. These towns hold the echoes of a Norman rather than a Celtic history. The land is good and has been cultivated for a long time; the houses are old and have been in families for generations. If this heritage lacks the dramatic power of the wild heroes of the legends, it is nonetheless equally worthy of preservation.

THE FIGHT AT THE FORD

The curse of Macha had come upon the men of Ulster. In their time of greatest need, they lay helpless on their backs, screaming and writhing in the pains of childbirth as the warrior goddess had prophesied. Only one man was free of it—this was Cú Chulainn, the warrior known as the Hound of Ulster, who though he was still but seventeen was already the greatest fighter the land of Ireland had ever known. The armies of Maeve of Connacht were marching forward, intent on capturing the Brown Bull of Cooley from Conchobhar Mac Neasa of Ulster, so that the queen's herd could be as fine and finer than that of her husband, Ailill. She sent hundreds of men against the hero Cú Chulainn and he killed them all, as effortlessly as a bull flicks away flies on a hot summer's day. Then, loath to lose so many good men, she chose great champions to meet the defender of Ulster in single combat where he held her army at bay at the ford on the River Dee. However, every day her champion was slain, and Cú Chulainn hurled insults at her across the river from where he camped with his charioteer and a small group of followers.

Maeve consulted with her council, and they all spoke with one voice—the only champion capable of defeating Cú Chulainn was Ferdia, who had trained with him at the warrior-queen Scáthach's school in Alba. However, when Maeve called Ferdia to her, he refused point blank to fight with Cú Chulainn, for not only was he the Hound's foster-brother, suckled by the same wet-nurse, long-time sharer of his secrets and his dreams of glory, but

Opposite: *A statue in Ardee depicting Cú Chulainn holding Ferdia in his arms, singing a lament for his dead companion.*

he loved the champion with the love of those who have suffered and fought together, in a bond closer than that of blood. Ferdia remembered their sense of comradeship as they ran wild through the woods in the glory of young freedom, before they took on the warrior's code; he remembered the mock battles that always ended in laughter, and although Maeve promised him gold and jewels and her own ripe body, he shook his head. In desperation, Maeve arranged a great feast. Whole cows were roasted, the finest of boars and the most succulent of deer. There was ale and wine, and Maeve's own special drink, mead—sweet and heavy as the honey from which it was made. Maeve plied Ferdia with good things and turned his head with praise, and finally she said, "You need not worry about your friend sharing your scruples, Ferdia. I have heard it said that he has mocked you, saying that it would not worry him to skewer you as well as the rest of the champions, and it would take no effort for him to do it."

Ferdia, fuddled with drink and flattery, shouted out, "Indeed, then I will fight him and change his tune."

So Maeve smiled coolly, and, promising him a great brooch and the body of her fair daughter, Fionnabhair, she left him to sleep off his hangover and remember his promise in the cold light of morning.

After all the court had retired to sleep, Fergus Mac Róich lay tossing and turning in his bed. Fergus had joined the Connacht camp because of Conchobhar Mac Neasa's treachery against the Sons of Usna, but he loved Cú Chulainn as a son. Finally, he got up and crept from the camp. He crossed to the other side of the river and warned the Hound that Ferdia was coming against him. Cú Chulainn lamented bitterly that he should be forced to fight his friend, but Fergus said, "Do not let your affection blind you. Ferdia will be the hardest of your enemies to defeat, for he wears the great skin of horn that shields him from every weapon."

"And do I not have the *Gáe Bolga*?" said Cú Chulainn proudly. "The great mace that goes into a man's flesh and splits into thirty darts, punching holes throughout his inside? Who can defeat that?"

And Cú Chulainn went that night to feast and sleep with his wife, Emer, in her fort at Dún Dealgan, so that none should say that he was afraid of the contest on the morrow.

In the pink and gold dawn, the champions faced each other through the mist on the river. They were dressed in their finest armour—the bronze and gold and silver glinted in the sun; their sleek horses whickered in welcome when they saw each other, and their charioteers called greetings over the water. When Ferdia, tall and brown-haired, saw the beloved face of Cú Chulainn, he bowed low, and Cú Chulainn, small and broad and dark, returned his bow.

"Greetings to you, Ferdia," said the Hound.

"And greetings to you, Hound of Ulster," said Ferdia.

"How shall we fight today?"

"Let us use the throwing spears and darts," said Ferdia.

So they fought, each one as skilled as the other. At first, it seemed to them almost like one of the games in Scáthach's training camp. They pitted skill against skill, each one knowing the tricks and feints that the other put forward. However, as the battle became more serious, they began to shout insults at each other. They dredged up all the old, hurtful names from the past...

"You were my little servant, Cú," whispered Ferdia as he held Cú Chulainn's neck in a vice-like grip. "My little bed-maker, my little shadow, copying me when I practised my skills, often not able to keep up with me."

"That was then; this is now; and it was only because you were years older than me," responded Cú Chulainn furiously, wrenching his neck out of the other's grasp and forcing him onto his knees in the river-bed. "Now I am the stronger, and you have lost many of your skills and half your strength through drinking mead and sleeping with loose women like Fionnabhair. Did Maeve promise you her? Sure that bitch is promised to every dog in the camp..."

"Is she indeed? Well, there's not so many women will want to sleep with you by the time I am finished with you, you black-visaged squint eye!"

"Ah shut up, bladder breath!"

"Gorse head!"

"Old lard-belly!"

But then Ferdia was wounded, and he caught and ripped open the Hound's arm; and by the time the sun went down, both champions were bleeding and exhausted. As they parted that night, they kissed each other fondly, and Cú Chulainn sent medicines over to the other side of the river to his friend, while Ferdia sent the best food from the Connacht camp to Cú Chulainn. Their horses shared the same paddock and their charioteers sat together at the same campfire. The next morning, the two champions rose and greeted each other across the bank. On this day, Ferdia gave Cú Chulainn the choice of weapons, so that they fought with javelins and spears. And that night too, Ferdia sent food, and Cú Chulainn sent healers to chant incantations over

Above:
The ford on the River Dee at Ardee.

Ferdia, for their wounds were so severe that salves or medicines could no longer heal them.

On the third day, they fought with swords, with such ferocity that the river stopped in its course, and those who watched from either side of the bank were covered in the blood of the champions as it sprayed from their veins. Most of the watchers fled in terror, and those who stayed could see little, only a whirling cloud of dust and blood, and sharp flames when the swords crashed against one another.

That evening, the two men did not embrace one another, but turned as soon as the sun went down and made their way wearily to their camps. There was no sharing of food or medicines, and the horses and charioteers stayed on opposite sides of the river. In the grey morning, the warriors made no greeting to each other as they watched each other perform feats of arms. Then they moved closer and closer to each other, so that they were fighting hand to hand, and only the charioteers had the courage to stay to watch the flesh and blood fly. They fought in utter silence.

As the evening drew in, they fought more and more furiously, so that their great bronze shields burst as they crashed together; and as this happened, and before Laeg, Cú Chulainn's charioteer, could hand Cú Chulainn another, Ferdia forced his sword into Cú Chulainn's chest, lifting him into the air on its point. He threw him towards the northern bank of the river, shouting, "Go home for your bone, Dog!"

Laeg, fearing that Cú Chulainn would be defeated, shouted. "Look you, Cú—he has tossed you like a mother tosses her baby!"

Then the battle fury came upon Cú Chulainn. He called to Laeg to bring the *Gáe Bolga*, and he whirled around with war demons circling him like black crows. Within seconds, the great mace had plunged into Ferdia's chest and pierced through the hide that covered it. He fell to the water, screaming in his last agony.

A moment later, Cú Chulainn, the battle-rage passed, had fallen beside his friend and lifted him in his arms, watching the life fade from his face. Ferdia's charioteer came forward to take the body, but Cú Chulainn dragged it, crawling himself and grievously wounded, onto the Ulster side of the river. The charioteer called, his voice broken in sorrow and shame, "Is it his weapons and armour you want? Take them then, but leave us the body so that it will not be mocked and shamed by the Ulster army."

Cú Chulainn looked up from where he lay on the ground, his face twisted with rage and grief: "Get away from this river before I kill you too, man. Ferdia will be buried with the honour of a prince and a great warrior; I will wash his fair body myself for the ceremony. It is not for the spoils of war I have taken him, but because I need to hold his head in my arms a last time, and a last time tell him how dear he was to me. No one could have had a truer friend or a braver companion. It is to me now as if I have killed a part of myself. I had thought of war as an honourable thing, not this bloody mess, brought on by the whims and greed of the great ones, and turning friend against friend. It seems to me now that every battle I ever fought was nothing—was the game of a child—compared to this one I fought with Ferdia, my beloved brother."

Cú Chulainn continued to defend Ulster against the armies of Connacht until the Ulster warriors were able to fight once again. For the origin of the Táin, *see "Pillow Talk"; for the end, see "The Battle of the Bulls." For the reason behind the sickness of the Ulstermen, see "Macha's Curse."*

Cooley, Louth

CUAILGNE

The Cooley peninsula carries resonances of past battles and ancient divisions. From the time of the great epic of the *Táin Bó Cuailgne* (*The Cattle Raid of Cooley*), it marked the borderland between Ulster and Leinster, north and south. To the north of the peninsula lies Newry, situated in Northern Ireland; to the south lies Dundalk, part of the Republic of Ireland. Yet it is, to an extent, a self-enclosed world of its own; the physical action of travelling from the urban sprawl of either town to the misty beauty of the hills gives the impression of leaving one world and entering another. It is very easy to imagine it as a self-enclosed kingdom. The town of Carlingford with its lovely harbour provides a pleasant base for time spent exploring the area. Once an important defensive town, Carlingford is of Norse origin and has preserved its ancient buildings to a degree that is unusual in

Irish towns. Its extensive remains include King John's Castle and a priory which was founded in 1305. Carlingford is a popular harbour for sailors and so it has also more modern attractions, with good restaurants and pubs full of character. However, its real attraction must remain the situation, between hills and sea, with easy access to the mountains and beautiful views over the inlet to the north.

The area is ideal for the hill-walker. The Táin Trail is a signed walking route of about 40 kilometres (25 miles) through the hills of the peninsula. From the blue mountains, with small roads winding over them, there are magnificent views of water to both north and south, and perhaps most memorably from the Black Mountain towards the north and the Mournes above Newry. There are numerous forests and marshy places off the high road over the mountains to Omeath. It was here, on this spine of hills, that the Donn (Brown Bull) of Cooley dashed his head against the rocks in his last agony. *Druim an Tairbh* (the "Back of the Bull"), the actual site where the Donn died as recorded in the *Táin,* has not yet been established, so any one of the hills has the potential to be that place.

There is evidence of population here from far into prehistory, with a large scattering of monuments in the area, particularly court cairns. One such monument, the Long Woman's Grave (now partially destroyed), has a story attached to it which demonstrates the particular humour of the local people. It is

Below:
H. Gastineau's engraving of Carlingford Lough, County Louth.

said that a prince brought his bride to the site and told her to look around her—that everything she could see was part of his possessions. Unfortunately, she looked the wrong way, could see only a few feet in front of her, and died of the shock! Not far away, on the grounds of Ballymascanlon Hotel golf course, is one of the finest portal dolmens in Ireland, the 3.6-metre (12-foot) high Proleek Dolmen.

The name Louth is said to come from Lugh, the many-skilled Celtic god who brought the Tuatha Dé Danann victory at the Battle of Moytura. This part of the county is very different from the area around prosperous Ardee, but the people still speak with the same slow musical accent, and still seem to take a long time in considering a basic question such as a request for directions. Perhaps such hesitation is a result of having been so long a people of the borderlands, between North and South, between Celt and Norman, between a world of quiet farms and lovely hills, and one of great heroism and tragic battles.

THE BATTLE OF THE BULLS

The last battle was over. The *Táin Bó Cuailgne*, the long war-tale that poets would recite for many centuries to come, had reached its end. Ulster was victorious over Connacht, although Queen Maeve, devious as ever, still had a trick or two up her sleeve. The smoke of funeral pyres covered the skies over the battlefield of Garach; the air was filled with the stench of burning bodies and the cries of ravens, who called to their comrades that red meat was littered on the battlefield, fresh for the taking. The war goddess Morrigan shrieked high above the smoke, while her sister Badbh took the form of a scald-crow and rejoiced in the mindless carnage that had come upon all who had fought that day. Men had slipped and slid in the blood and gore that covered the green fields; their heads had been cut off them where they lay. Bones and gobbets of flesh lay scattered like bloody stars over the black earth; skulls lay split in pieces; bodies had been dismantled into their component parts; and now arms and legs and feet and hands lay yards from each other, as if they had never been attached to the same living, breathing person. Here and there, a headless torso was sprawled, spitted with spears. It was too soon for those who had been in the battle to feel sorrow, for all anyone wanted to do was to get away from the smell of rotting and burning flesh and the shrieks of those who had not yet met with the mercy of great Donn, the Lord of Death.

Long-faced Maeve had begun her journey back to her palace of Cruachain at Rathcroghan in the west, defeated by the armies of the north and having had her own life saved only by the mercy of Cú Chulainn. She left widows and orphans wailing behind her and brought back to her people in Connacht news of many deaths, but she walked with a proud step, for had she not managed to take the Donn of Cooley back with her? The night before the final ignominious battle with Conchobhar, Maeve had sent the Donn to Rathcroghan with his fifteen heifers, by hidden ways and through trackless wastes. She had looked around at the battlefield and called it a shame and a shambles, but deep within her heart, she did not feel grief, for she had the bull—the greatest bull in Ireland, perhaps in the history of the world. The storytellers would speak of his prowess for years to come—how his back was broad enough to take thirty lads on it; how he could fill fifty heifers in a day, and, if they did not have a calf by the following morning, they would burst from the power of his seed within them.

Above:
The Cooley Peninsula, County Louth.

As they made their way through the blue hills and brown bogs, Maeve began to hum gently, already planning her revenge on Cú Chulainn. The sun was shining and her head was full of plans to build up her army again. Her husband, Ailill, walking silently beside her, almost tripped over a severed head. It was one left behind from their journey north—one of the thousands of

Connachtmen killed by Cú Chulainn. It was now staring at Ailill with empty eye-sockets. From the red hair and the golden torc at the throat, he recognised his sister's son. He turned off the trail and was sick.

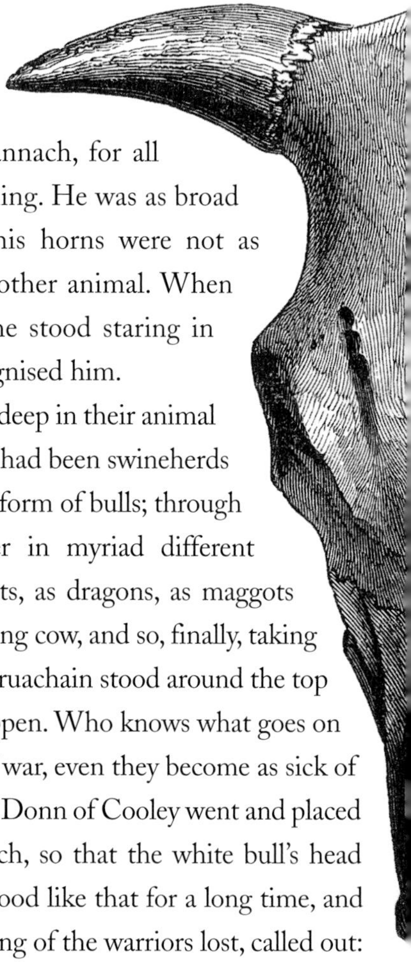

Back at Rathcroghan, the bull was led to where the white bull, Finnbheannach, was held within an earthen compound. No one would venture in to feed Finnbheannach, for all through the battle he had been like a wild thing. He was as broad as the Donn of Cooley, though perhaps his horns were not as massive. He had never been defeated by another animal. When the Donn was brought into the stockade, he stood staring in front of him, pawing the ground as if he recognised him.

The two bulls faced each other. Somewhere, deep in their animal brains, each knew the smell of the other. They had been swineherds together many lives before they had taken the form of bulls; through centuries they had battled with each other in myriad different bodies—as fish, as stags, as warriors, as ghosts, as dragons, as maggots together in the one stream, swallowed by a young cow, and so, finally, taking the form of bulls. The people of the court of Cruachain stood around the top of the stockade, waiting to see what would happen. Who knows what goes on in an animal's head? Perhaps after centuries of war, even they become as sick of slaughter as humans. Whatever the reason, the Donn of Cooley went and placed his hoof gently on the horn of Finnbheannach, so that the white bull's head bowed to the ground as if to his master. He stood like that for a long time, and the people grew weary of waiting. Ailill, thinking of the warriors lost, called out: "Will you not give us something to see, Donn of Cooley? Men have died on both sides because of you."

At that, the brown one bellowed out and the two beasts locked horns. It was as if a great storm had erupted out of nowhere—the noise like thunder, the earth flying on all sides whipped up by the giant hooves. The bulls crashed through the stockade, killing Bricriu, the satirist who was looking on to judge the fight, and then churned earth under their hooves as, horns locked, they began their battle through the length and breadth of Ireland, leaving lakes dug from the soil and hills raised with their fighting.

There was terror throughout Connacht, for many thought that the world had come to an end. There was no possibility of sleep, because of the noise of the fighting bulls. All who heard it could never forget it, for it seemed as if the sky was filled with the sounds of angry gods bellowing their rage. The battle lasted for a day and a night; finally, at dawn, the people at Cruachain saw the Donn passing with the great body of his rival caught on his horns. However, the Donn himself was sorely wounded, spilling blood with every step he took, leaving hoof prints filled with gore. He staggered into the lake near the *dún* as if to try to wash off the carcass of his rival, but came out with the liver and shoulder blade and loins still caught on his great black horns. It seemed to Ailill's troops that they might now be able to take the bull and kill him, but Fergus Mac Róich, the Ulster warrior who had fled to Connacht when the sons of Usna were killed, roared out: "The Brown of Ulster is the victor, and half-dead already. All of you leave him in peace and let him go back to his own place now, or be answerable to me."

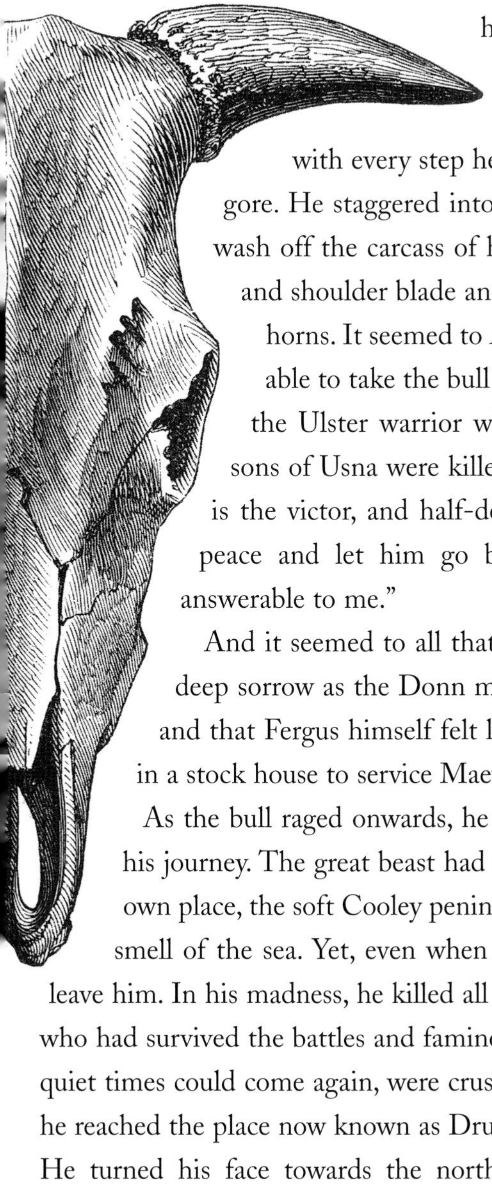

Centre:
Head of an ox, discovered in bogland at Dunshaughlin, County Meath.

And it seemed to all that Fergus's eyes followed him in some deep sorrow as the Donn made his way back towards the north; and that Fergus himself felt like a bull trapped in Connacht, kept in a stock house to service Maeve.

As the bull raged onwards, he dropped parts of Finnbheannach on his journey. The great beast had only one instinct—to get back to his own place, the soft Cooley peninsula with its gentle hills and the fresh smell of the sea. Yet, even when he reached there, his frenzy did not leave him. In his madness, he killed all that stood in his way. Many of those who had survived the battles and famine and sickness, and now thought that quiet times could come again, were crushed underfoot by his hooves. Finally, he reached the place now known as Druim an Tairbh, the "Back of the Bull." He turned his face towards the north and rushed into the flank of the mountain before him, as if he thought it was yet another rival to vanquish. But his horns locked into the soil and the rock, and his heart burst in his chest like a nut cracking. He fell to the earth, his spirit leaving his body with a great bellow of rage and pain. It was many days before even the ravens dared to approach his great carcass to feed on the rotting flesh.

Cú Chulainn was finally killed through the machinations of Maeve. At his death, he tied himself to a stone so that he would die upright, facing his enemies.

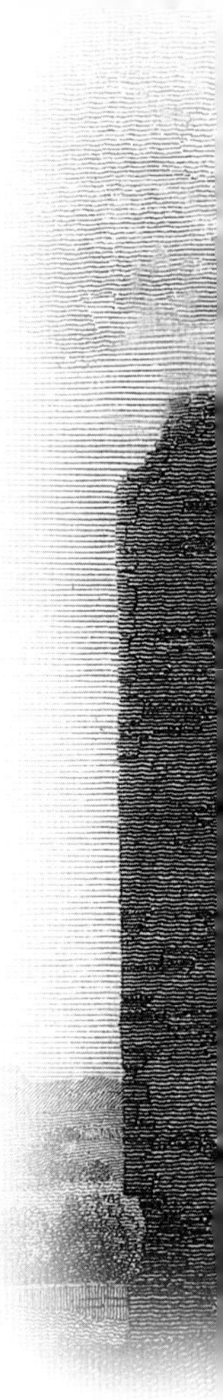

Tara, Meath

TEAMHAIR

Tara is probably the most famous legendary site in Ireland. Its name, *Teamhair*, means "Lofty Place." It is associated with days of glory: with heroes and beautiful women, with great priest-kings who ruled a land that in the legends was always fertile and contented. Yet by the time these legends were being written down by Christian scholars, Tara was already no more than grass-covered mounds. Its glory days were long over and its secrets hidden under the earth. Nonetheless, standing on these mounds and looking over the magnificent views of Meath to all sides, you get a sense of the power of the old kings—for Tara was the heart of all that symbolised royalty and prosperity to the ancient Celts.

Tara is an important location in many of the most important stories of Ireland, including tales of both love and war. Here the kings mated with the goddess of

sovereignty at the beginning of their reign. Here every year on the three days either side of Samhain—the feast of the dead at the Celtic New Year in November—the doors to the other world swung open and here, every third year, a great assembly was held. Here, Conn of the Hundred Battles stood on the Stone of Destiny, the *Lia Fáil*, which cried under his foot because he was the rightful king. Here, Cormac, the great high king of Ireland, found the path to the realm of Manannán, the god of the sea, and here began the tragic story of Diarmaid and Gráinne, Cormac's daughter who fell in love with Diarmaid at her wedding feast. Here too reigned Niall of the Nine Hostages—tradition says that it was he who brought Patrick to Ireland as a slave. When Patrick returned many years later as a missionary, he defied the power of Tara and King Laoghaire by lighting a fire on Easter Sunday on nearby Slane Hill. Then he and his followers, magically transforming themselves into a flock of deer, made their way secretly up onto the hill of Tara, into the sacred space, and challenged the king's druids to a combat of magical powers. (This transformation is the reason why the prayer "St. Patrick's Breastplate" is also known as "The Deer's

Above:
St. Patrick's Church on the Hill of Tara.

Cry.") Patrick's victory gave him the right to preach the gospel in Ireland, and the power of the old ways was weakened forever. The final desertion of Tara is said to have been the result of the place being cursed by a saint.

Tara is entered through a gate leading to the nineteenth-century church which replaced a much older church on the site, and is now used as an interpretative centre. The climb up the hill is a gradual one, the grass kept cropped by sheep. The Fort of the Synods, Ráth na Riogh, Teach Cormac, Ráth Gráinne and Ráth Laoghaire—the names given to the monuments on the hill—date from a later period than the monuments themselves, but the *Lia Fáil* is said to be the same stone which called out when Conn touched it.

Modern excavations have been carefully limited in order to preserve the integrity of the site, but ongoing archaeological surveys reinforce the image of Tara as a hugely important ceremonial site, which by the Iron Age had become associated strongly with royalty. The Mound of the Hostages covers a 4,000-year-old passage grave—the remains of 200 cremations were found here. As in so many places in Ireland, the spiritual power of the site came from its having been considered sacred for thousands of years, and built upon by generation after generation. In historical times, the Uí Néill clan claimed Tara as the site of the high kingship. There are two wells near the site, and an ancient hawthorn tree where people still tie rags as an offering and make their wishes. On the River Odder nearby, King Cormac is said to have built the first mill in Ireland for his mistress, Cernat, to save her the pain of grinding corn when she was carrying his child.

There is layer upon layer of ancient ritual embodied in this landscape, but the feeling of Tara is not of the weight of centuries, but of free air—of a green landscape smiling upwards with the promise of a good summer. Close to the great ceremonial centre of the Boyne, where forces older than human ones hold sway, this is the heart of a civilised, almost courtly, prehistory.

"She was the sacred place on the road of life"—so runs the scholar Edward Gwynn's translation of the *Dindshenchas*, the lore of place. In other poems, Tara is described as the noblest of hills, a rampart of glory and gold, a centre of feastings and battles. There are times, especially at those ancient lynchpins of the Celtic year, the first day of May (Bealtaine) and at Halloween (Samhain), when Tara is still visited by those trying to make a connection with its glorious past. However, most of the time, Tara is a quiet, green hill with a view of stud-farms and lazy cattle, of a blue, hazy distance and a quietness broken, not by the call of the land to its sovereign, but only by the sound of birds singing.

THE MAGIC BRANCH

The great high king of Ireland, Cormac Mac Airt, stood and looked over the fair green of Tara. It was a pleasant prospect on this May morning, for the dawn light changed the pastures to the colour of gold, and a land of plenty stretched before him—a rich, contented land of fat cows and fast horses, of valorous deeds and great hunts. It was a land of sweet music, of songs which celebrated the feats of heroes, but it was also a land full of the quieter music of mill wheels and spinning wheels, of easy prosperity. Cormac had little cause for complaint, for had he not a son growing in strength and courage, and a fair daughter whose gentleness and dignity would make her a fitting wife for any hero? Had he not a clever wife, whose beauty had not faded with the years, and even a small, dark-eyed mistress who asked no difficult questions and let him lie with his head on her lap while she sang to him for hour after hour? Why then was he, in the prime of life and at the height of his power, dissatisfied and weary, as he looked over the flower-covered green? Was it because there were no more battles to fight and no more women to win? He had won them all—he had tasted wine and blood and kisses—and here he stood, watching the sun rise over the lands that lay under his control like some sweetly smiling woman, and wondering why he felt empty greyness in his heart. He stood, stroking his dark beard, wishing for something to which he could not put a name.

Then he heard it—a sound like no other sound he had ever heard, in either the banqueting hall or the forest; a music that seemed to sound in stillness rather then in movement or time, with a sweetness that filled his heart so that he felt it contract in his chest. The music grew louder and he saw a young man coming towards him. He was tall, with golden hair, and he was clad in a purple cloak with green and silver lining that caught the sun and seemed to sparkle as he walked. In his hand, he held a silver branch with three golden apples on it, and as he shook it gently, it seemed that the music came from it. Cormac greeted the stranger courteously.

"Fair youth, you are welcome here to my kingdom. What is your name and station?"

The stranger smiled and shook the branch again, so that all rational thought went from Cormac's head, and he thought only that he would die if he did not have the source of that wonderful music.

Above:
The Lia Fáil, *or Stone of Destiny, at Tara, which cries out at the touch of the rightful king of Ireland.*

"Fair youth," he addressed the stranger again. "Tell me what I must give you to have that wonderful branch. From where does it come?"

Now the young man spoke, and his voice had the music of the apple-branch in it.

"It comes from the Isle of Apples, from the Pleasant Plain, from the Land beneath the Waves. It comes from the kingdom of Manannán Mac Lir. It is a branch of great power, for when you shake it, everyone who hears it forgets the sorrow of the world in the delight of its music. And you may have it, if you grant me three wishes."

Cormac did not stop to consider. He said, "That I agree to; only let me have the branch."

The stranger smiled and put the branch in the high king's hand. Then he said, "I will come back to you in a year to ask for my first wish."

A year later, to the very day, Cormac went out onto the green and saw the youth coming towards him, looking as young and as fine as ever. When he reached Cormac, he said, "I have come to ask for my first wish."

"Speak then," said Cormac, who had had time to consider and was a little nervous of what the stranger might ask.

"I will have your daughter come with me," said the stranger.

Cormac paled, for he loved his daughter, Ailbe, as pastures love the soft rain after a hot day's sunshine.

"I will give you fields and fine horses and bondmaids. I will give you gold and jewels and the treasures of my palace. Ask me anything, but do not ask for my daughter."

But the stranger shook his head to all of Cormac's promises, and when he realised that he had no choice, the king called his daughter from the hall and embraced her tenderly, weeping as she left with the stranger.

"I will return next year for my next wish," said the youth. There was great mourning in Tara until Cormac shook the magic branch, and all sorrow was forgotten.

The next year, Cormac met the stranger again, and this time he asked for his son, which made the king weep bitterly, for he loved his son, Cairbre Lifeachair, as the pastures love the sun after a long winter's cold.

"I will give you all my kingdom," he said, "if you will only let my son stay." But the stranger shook his head, so Cormac sent his son with the stranger, and went back to the manor of Tara, where he and his wife wept long and hard; and all the people of Tara wept, until he shook the branch with the golden apples, and he could no longer hear their weeping.

The third year, the stranger asked of Cormac his wife. The king bent his head and wept, for he loved his wife, Eithne, as the pastures love the sun and the rain together; and he said, "Take my life; for I have nothing if my children and my wife are gone."

But again the stranger smiled and shook his head, and said, "Why do you not use your branch to forget your sorrow?"

Cormac said, "I will give you back your branch if you will give me back what I love. No magic nor music can heal sorrow and regret—it only makes us forget them for a time. If you will not give me back my family, I will go to your palace and die in the attempt to bring them home."

The golden-haired man said nothing, but merely smiled and took Cormac's wife's hand to lead her away.

And so Cormac followed the stranger into the mist that formed around him as he left the green of Tara. He walked for many miles, with the stranger striding ahead, leading his wife, and Cormac following, always following, over harsh mountains and rough bog, past fields of rushes filled with golden light, and always southwards into the sun, so that the two figures ahead seemed to walk in a halo of light.

He saw many wonderful sights as he made his journey, for he had stepped across the border into the land of the Sídh. He saw white horses race as easily across the surface of the sea as they would over the plains of Tara. He saw magical islands with castles and herds and brave, noble people. Finally, he came to a beautiful silver house, thatched with the feathers of white birds. In the courtyard outside there was a great fountain, and from it five streams of silver flowed. Over the fountain there were nine hazel bushes and five silver salmon swam in the waters below. A couple sat on high thrones behind the fountain; one was a glorious queen with golden hair and a crown of golden fishes with ruby eyes, and the other was the young man who had led Cormac's wife and children away.

Cormac saluted them and said, "What is this kingdom, and where am I?"

The queen smiled and said, "You have come to the Isle of Apples, the Pleasant Plain, the Land of Truth, Cormac of Ireland. This is where your family is; and you should know that they have been safe and happy since the time they came here. It is to them as if they have passed no more than a day with the people of Manannán, Ruler of the Ocean and the lord who sits here beside me."

Cormac bowed to her; for he knew that he was looking on the great goddess, Áine; and then, turning to the young man, he said, "Know then, King, that I would return to you this magic branch and all its wondrous music if you would give me back my loved ones. For not all the music in the world can make up for the loss of those who are dear to us. Or if you will not return them to me, I will stay here and give up my kingdom to be with them."

Then Manannán, who changed as he spoke from a young man to a man of great years and wisdom, bearded and white-haired, and with a crown of prancing silver horses with sapphire eyes, said, "No, King. Go back to your own place, and learn to be a wise king as well as a powerful one. You have been led here to learn what your next task is, which is to seek true judgement through the last years of your life. Take your family with you, for now you have learned to value them also. I will let you keep the Branch of Sweetness, but I will give you another gift also, the Cup of Truth, which will break in three pieces when three falsehoods are spoken over it, but become whole again when three true things are said."

Cormac and his family feasted that night with the god and goddess, eating their fill and listening to poets and musicians and talking to each other.

When Cormac awoke the next morning, he found himself on the green outside the ramparts of Tara. The air was full of the scent of cowslips and bluebells, and the sound of small birds singing in the dawn. The wonderful branch was there by his side, and the cup that had stood on Manannán's table; and all his family were with him, each one changed and made wiser by their sojourn in the Isle of Apples. After this time, Cormac became known as Cormac of the Long Beard, one of the greatest kings Ireland had ever known, wise and merciful; and during his reign Ireland was a golden land, rich and peaceful and full of music. For added to the music of spinning wheels and mill wheels and the clarion calls of hunts and quests, the deep music of the king's good judgement was heard in every valley in the land.

And there are those who say that even still, the deep sigh which cows make when they lie down on the grass on a fine summer's evening is one of regret and remembrance for those happy days when Cormac ruled over Ireland.

Newgrange and the Boyne Valley, Meath

BRÚ NA BÓINNE

If Tara is air and the flight of birds, Newgrange is wood and stone and water. If Tara is the sovereignty of the king, Newgrange is the sacred space far more powerful and more ancient than any sovereign's power. The concentration of great tombs at the bend of the River Boyne in County Meath (*Brú na Bóinne*, "The Mansion or dwelling Place on the Boyne," also translated as "The Bend of the Boyne") constitutes one of the most important centres of Neolithic antiquities in Ireland, and indeed in Europe. To reach Newgrange, you move slowly down roads which follow the bends of the river, past old stone farmhouses half-covered in green moss, through a landscape that has been cultivated by man from a time beyond time—a rich land, a quiet people; long before Maeve led her armies towards Ulster in battle for a great bull, the people here herded their cattle quietly, paying homage to the Bóinn, the cow-goddess of the river. The remains at Newgrange are from long before the time of the Celtic warrior society that produced the stories of the *Táin*. Knowth and Newgrange have been dated through excavation to around 2500BC, making them older than Stonehenge, Mycenae or the pyramids of Egypt. The Newgrange site remained sacred, a burial place for pre-Christian kings, and known and honoured at least until Roman times, but at some point after this the secrets of the mounds were lost. Newgrange became part of the possessions of the monks of Mellifont Abbey, a grassy hill for grazing cattle. The great tombs slipped quietly into the quiet land of Meath, and were left without interference until the beginning of the modern age. Then, at the end of the seventeenth century, a local landowner was quarrying stone, and stumbled onto the entrance to the chamber of the great mound at Newgrange.

Since then, the mound has been continuously studied, and, in the middle of the last century, Newgrange was excavated and the exterior reconstructed in line with the evidence available. Now the great mound is a sparkling white quartz-covered circle on the green hillside. Newgrange is one of many mounds in the Brú na Bóinne complex. It is the largest and most dramatic of the tombs, sited on a hill looking down towards the river, with its entrance aligned towards the mid-winter solstice sunrise. Before the archaeologists had discovered the alignment of the roof-box over the entrance to the great passage, situated so that it lights the

Below:
The River Boyne.

furthest recess in the tomb at dawn on the winter solstice, they had been told of a local tradition that held that the rising sun at some point in the year lit those same three spiral stones. The astronomical and engineering skills of a people who lived almost 5,000 years ago have also resulted in a structure that keeps the inner space as dry as a bone and silent as a tomb, where the temperature stays at a steady 10 degrees.

The other main ritual centres of the Boyne complex are Knowth and Dowth. Unlike Newgrange with its single mound, at Knowth you can spend time wandering through the ritual area marked by seventeen satellite mounds scattered around the central tomb. It is now also possible to visit the inside of this central mound. While Newgrange has one passage leading into the burial chamber, Knowth has two long passages leading into the centre under the great mound. Its orientation is hotly disputed, with theories put forward of equinoctical or possibly even lunar alignment. It should be visited as part of a trip to the complex, not least because the carved stones here are incredible examples of Megalithic art—in fact, the Knowth tombs constitute 30 percent of the known Megalithic art of Europe. Newgrange and Knowth can be visited only as part of a guided tour from the excellent interpretative centre, and as there is limited access, it makes sense to come very early in the day.

The visitor centre supplies a wealth of archaeological information. The archaeologists can tell us that while there is evidence of burials in the mounds, it seems highly

Below: *Plan of the gallery at Newgrange, County Meath.*

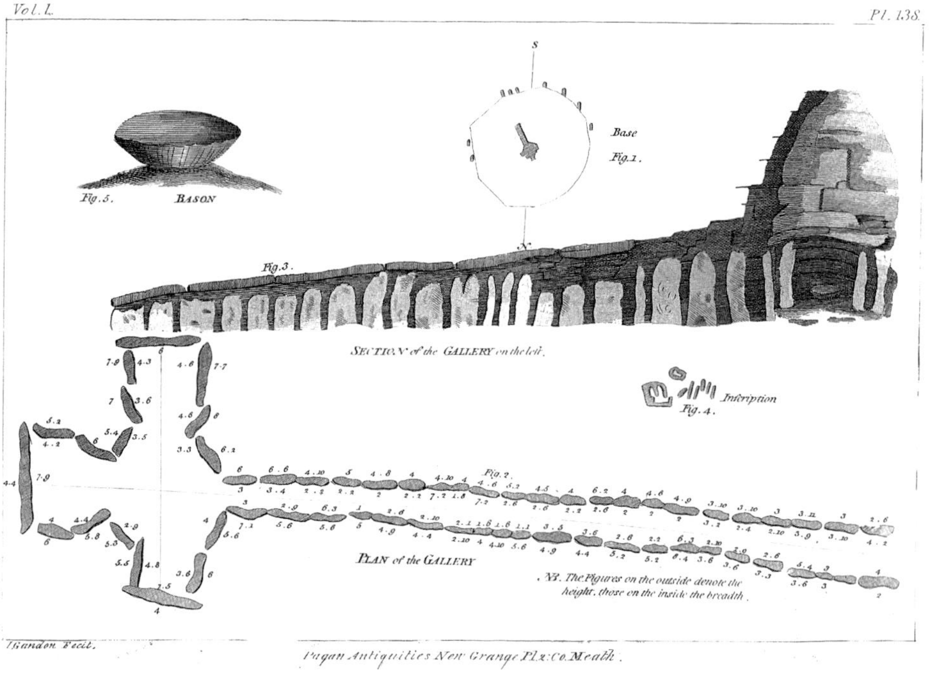

unlikely that these huge, complex structures were built as individual tombs. They can also give us a great deal of information on how these structures were made. However, what they cannot give us is definitive answers as to the meaning behind all this human effort. The experts cannot say *why* these people carved rocks with spirals, with lozenges, and, in one case, with a single fern. They cannot say why the stones were painstakingly shaped and carried from districts far away. Why did these people make the bowl-like depressions in the recess stones, which may have held some form of liquid? Are the carvings on the stones astronomical maps or messages in some lost shamanistic language that we can no longer read? Is the carving on the stone marking the western entrance of the main tomb at Knowth, resembling so closely a human face with an open, screaming mouth, the "guardian stone" as it has been named, or something else completely? In the absence of definitive scientific answers, theories abound.

What is sure is that these places acted as treasuries for the people who lived 5,000 years ago—treasuries not of material wealth, but of their deepest feelings and thoughts about how the cosmos functioned. If we take our leave of the archaeologists and go back to the legends, we are told that Aonghus, the young god, the god of lovers, brought the beloved dead to the Brú. Here he took Diarmaid and breathed life into him for a time every day so that he could converse with him in the dark house of the dead. Here, in this same chamber, light breaks in on the darkest day of the year. Here, by some power of love—whether human, emanating from the memory of the tribe, or divine, emanating from the power of their gods—here, in some sense, the dead lived and spoke to the living.

Close to Newgrange and a further integral part of the Brú na Bóinne complex was the royal house of Cleiteach, although there are conflicting theories about its exact location. Some authorities site it near Stackallen Bridge, which is located some miles from Newgrange on the Boyne. This is the theory put forward by the great nineteenth-century Gaelic scholar and place-name expert John O'Donovan, who suggests this place as a possibility in his Ordnance Survey letters. However, O'Donovan was not at all adamant about this theory; originally he sited Cleiteach at Clady, a hill on the northern bank of the Boyne, one mile north of Bective; later, he admitted that this must be wrong, and walked the length of the river trying to find the site. It was then that he put forward the possibility of Cletty being one of the mounds on the river near Stackallen at Broadboyne bridge. Later in the century, William Wilde, father of the famous Oscar, suggested either Clady or Assay as possible sites. There was little further investigation until Elizabeth Hickey, in 1965, made a convincing argument about the location of Cleiteach, based on geographical features and the physical landscape linked with the written sources, suggesting that the site of Cleiteach might be at Rosnaree House, near Newgrange itself.

Rosnaree, the wooded headland of the kings, is the place where the great high king, Cormac, is believed to be buried. He moved to Cleiteach from Tara after he gave up the high kingship because of physical disability, and died there when a salmon bone caught in his throat. At his funeral, as he was carried across the River Boyne, it rose up, refusing to let him be buried with the pagan kings at Newgrange. According to some accounts, Cleiteach is also the place where the god Nuadhu lived when banished from Newgrange by Aonghus Óg, and also where Fionn tasted the Salmon of Knowledge and gained the power of foreseeing.

Perhaps the specific site of the original Cleiteach, which was destroyed in a great fire in the sixth century during the reign of Muircheartach Mac Earca, is not really so important. The course of the River Boyne itself has been much altered by canalisation and by dredging. Its leafy banks, however, still repay the visitor with a sense of luxuriant, slow-moving power. Because it can sometimes be hard to connect with the ancient power of Newgrange, surrounded as we are by other people during the visit, it is worthwhile to spend time at the quieter places along the banks of the river. To visit the ancient graveyard at Ardmulchan, for example, when evening light turns the grass to a golden green, and to watch the river as it curves past the Norman castle and Celtic crosses, is to feel something akin to the kind of power that one feels at Knockainey in Limerick. In both these places, the land is rich and has been cultivated for a very long time, and the goddess that was honoured here is one associated with fertile land and herds. In one story, Bóinn, the goddess of the Boyne and mother of Aonghus, the Lord of Newgrange, was drowned and became the river when she opened the well of Segais. This mythical well was the source of wisdom where the nine hazel trees grew and dropped their nuts and berries in the water, there to be swallowed by the salmon of wisdom, the salmon which gave Fionn his powers of foreseeing. Bóinn flowed past Brú na Bóinne, one of the most important access points to the otherworld. And it had been at the Brú that she had betrayed her husband Elcmar when she lay with the Daghdha. On a night which the Daghdha made last for years, their mating engendered Aonghus. The *Dindshenchas*, the lore of places, calls on Bóinn as one of the great ones, the rulers of the landscape. Her name associates her strongly with cows (*bó* being the Irish word for cow), and there are echoes of her power well into the nineteenth century when O'Donovan recorded that local farmers drove their cattle through the River Boyne as a charm against the powers of the Sídh.

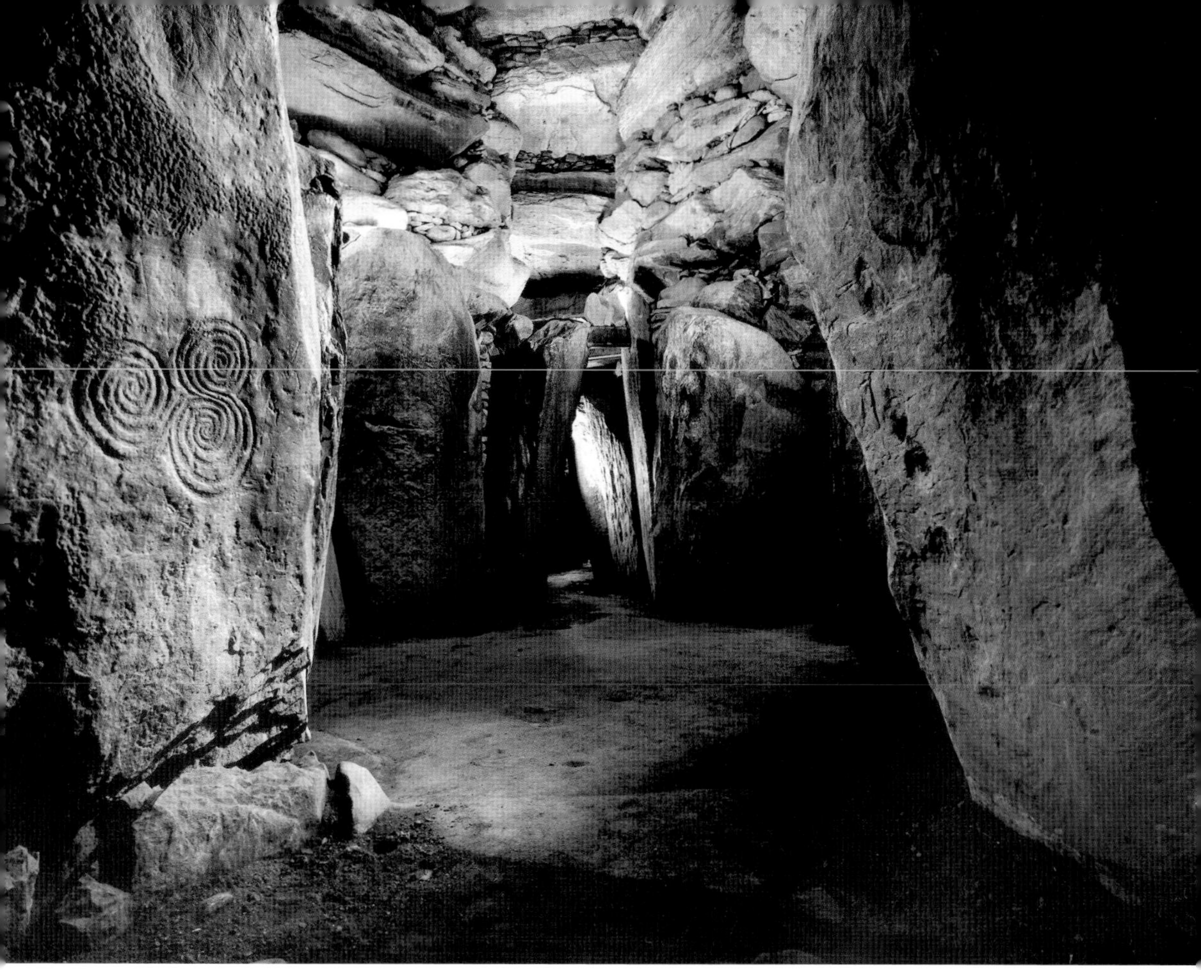

In historical times, the river was the site of the famous and bloody Battle of the Boyne between James II and William of Orange. Walking along its quiet banks, it is hard to imagine any violence or hatred disturbing the peaceful realm of this gentle goddess. However, the following story shows that things could be otherwise.

Above: *Sunlight floods the passage grave at Newgrange.*

THE REVENGE OF SÍN

When the great king, Muircheartach Mac Erca, came back from a hunting trip with a strange and beautiful woman, there was much talking among his people, for it was whispered that she had appeared out of nowhere while he sat apart from his companions on the hunting mound at the Brú. Many thought that she must be a fairy woman come out of the mounds, for her beauty seemed not of this world. It was a dangerous thing to do—to hunt alone at the time of Samhain, when the leaves were turning and beginning to fall in fiery drifts, and the great forests on the banks of the Boyne were transformed into a copper and crimson melting pot. Outside the houses, cold air solidified into a mist when man or beast breathed out, mingling with the vapour that rose from the river. Inside the houses, there were great fires and feasts, and songs celebrating a king whose victories had brought all the tribes under his power, who had left dead bodies as countless as the leaves that fell from the trees, crushed underfoot into the earth. A tall, dark-haired man with a heavy beard and a searching eye, Muircheartach was generous and hospitable; his house at Cletty was always full of guests, of poets and musicians and brave warriors.

The people loved and trusted their king; so although they whispered when the woman came to Cletty, they did not demur. However, when Muircheartach put his wife, Duaibhseach, and his own children out of the house, his people began to worry that he was under an enchantment that would bring evil to the realm. And while the woman, Sín, was indeed beautiful, with her slanted amber eyes and bronze hair, it was a strange, sly beauty, a beauty without gentleness, and her power over the king was such that he could do nothing but watch her while she moved or spoke or sang. Then the king commanded that, at his beloved's request, no cleric should enter Cletty while the lady Sín resided there.

Duaibhseach, proud and a princess in her own right, went, red-eyed, to the hermit Cairneach and complained of her treatment, and he went and stood in front of the great house—one of the finest and strongest in Ireland—and cursed Muircheartach for his evil-doing.

However, Sín, looking from the ramparts with Muircheartach, laughed and said to the king, "Do not worry about the curse the greasy cleric puts on you. He cannot harm you with his bells and his books while I am here to protect you, for my magic is stronger than his."

Muircheartach looked at her lovely form, and thought of the knowledge that she had, which he thirsted after as he might after wine or her body, and asked the question he had wanted to ask from the first moment he had seen her: "Are you human, then, or a woman of the Sídh?"

Sín smiled and said, "I am human like you, but I have knowledge that could make wonders happen before your eyes. I could make the Boyne water into wine, and change the very stones on the hills into flocks of sheep, and the ferns that grow all around Cletty into fat swine. Ask me what you will."

So Muircheartach asked her to perform these deeds, and before his eyes she changed the stones around the *dún* into blue men who battled with another army which she made from goats—a horrible goblin crew which had kept their animal heads, horns and all, but had the bodies of warriors. It was a brave battle the couple watched, and when it was over, Sín brought the king and his household inside and took three casks of water which she changed into a wine the like of which the king had never before tasted. Then she fed the host with magic swine which she had created from ferns. It was a wild feast that night, but one that gave those that partook of it no nourishment. The next day, the king and his army could hardly move from their beds, for their strength had been sapped by the enchanted food and drink.

Now, Sín had power over the king and all his court, so it seemed to them that battalions of the blue men and other creatures without heads were attacking the house, and the king and his warriors went out to do battle with this phantom army, not realising that the witch had made the demons of stones and sods and the green growing things of the riverbank. So it continued, with the king moving further and further into a world of dark enchantment—feasting at night on magic food that left him weak in the morning, and further weakened during the day by the senseless battling with the goblin army created by Sín. The clerics tried to cure him of the enchantment, but as soon as he returned to Sín, his eyes were blinded once again.

This went on, then, until the Wednesday night after All Saints' Day, when a winter wind came over the land, and Sín called out her names of Sigh and Wind and Winter, Storm and Grief. First, thunder and lightning flashed, and then she made a great snowstorm come down, which enveloped the house at Cletty and the sleeping king. He awoke screaming in the darkness, having seen fire and destruction, forewarning him of the fate that he was bringing upon himself. Twice he awoke from nightmares but each time the lady Sín gave him enchanted wine and he fell back into a drugged sleep. The third time, he awoke to find the house ablaze, and all his retainers fled, for as he slept, Sín had lit red fires in every corner of the mansion. She had put each weapon in the place with its point facing inward and had set a demon army battling outside, so that the king thought that the house was surrounded by enemies. Fire burst from every doorpost and window ledge. Muircheartach ran around in frenzy, trying to find a way out, but everywhere was blocked by flame and crashing timbers. The flickering leaves of the fire fell on his head and his shoulders, and terror came into his heart—a terror that he had never known in battle. Yet still the frenzy that Sín had put on him clouded his brain and his eyes, so that everywhere he looked he saw someone ready to attack him, and he fought the very tables and benches wildly, as if they had been mortal enemies.

Muircheartach begged Sín to save him, to make a path for him through the flames, but she turned her back and disappeared. With her cloak of invisibility about her, Sín stood and watched, until the flames grew too hot and bright and she left Muircheartach to his fate. He ran screaming through the house, the flames biting at him like angry teeth. Finally, in desperation, he climbed into a cask of wine, but the flames fell on his head, and burnt it, leaving the rest of his body whole. So it was said that the king was both burned and drowned.

Cairneach buried Muircheartach with the respect due to a great king. Duaibhseach came to her husband's graveside and lamented, and they say that she finally fell dead from grief. Then the clerics saw a most beautiful lady approaching them—so lovely that some of them turned their eyes to the ground to keep their minds from evil thoughts, while others could not look away from her. Long red hair fell over a green mantle with a silver fringe, and her beautiful countenance was made even lovelier by the loneliness and sadness of her face.

"Who are you?" they asked.

"I am Sín, daughter of King Sige. I am the one who brought this king to his death."

"And why did you do this?" they asked.

"Muircheartach, dead here before you, killed my father and my mother and my sister at the battle of Cerb; he destroyed all my family, all the old tribes of Tara, and took the land of my people away from them. I was only a child when that happened, but I swore that I would gain vengeance on him and I learned the skills of magic so that I could do so." She paused, and the face she turned to Cairneach was the bleakest he had ever seen.

"But despite all my knowledge and foreseeing, what I did not know was that I myself would fall under a spell—that I would love this man for his strength and his courage, his kindness and generosity; for his smile and the way the hair curled at the back of his neck. That is the revenge fate has had upon me."

It is said that then she too died, from her grief at the death that she herself had brought about, and that although she had been an enchantress and the murderer of a great king, because of her beauty and her sorrow, Cairneach took pity on her and buried her in hallowed ground.

Hill of Uisneach, Westmeath

UISNEACH

Uisneach Hill has always been considered the centre of Ireland in both physical and metaphysical terms. In legendary terms, it stands in the province of Midhe, the mythical fifth province which touches all of the four others. The hill is located in Westmeath, a county that has been described as Meath's less fortunate twin, for here the land is not so rich. Uisneach is not a high or commanding hill, standing only 181 metres (594 feet) above sea level. Yet the view encompasses the central plain and, like at Tara and Cruachain, it is not necessary to climb very high to see very far. The hill was excavated in 1926 and a layer of ash found at the southern end of the ring ditch, indicating that great fires were lit here over long periods, from Neolithic to historical times. Excavations have shown that Iron Age structures were also built here, but most of the remains on the hill are little more to the naked eye than mounds and earthen circles. The hill's most impressive feature is not man-made at all, but the great boulder on the south-west side of the hill, known as the Catstone. This huge, cracked limestone boulder was left in the valley after the retreat of the ice, and is 5 metres (16 feet) high—all the more dramatic because it is surrounded by green fields. The stone is easily reached from the Mullingar–Athlone road, on a track which on our visit in early autumn led past blue flowers and pink thistles, reddening hawthorn berries and already ripened blackberries. It is a quiet place without the great dramatic beauty of the west, but it is also mercifully unspoilt by any development, and its sense of apartness was increased by the fact that when we visited there were no animals grazing on the hill. The Catstone's ancient name was the Stone of Divisions or *Aill na Mireann*; it marked the true centre of Ireland and is reputed to be the place where Eriu (also called Éire) is buried, the goddess from whom Ireland gets one of its names.

The hill has one of the greatest concentrations of legends in Ireland. In some accounts, it was on this hill that the god Lugh was attacked by three enemies—the three brothers who married the triple goddesses of which Eriu was one part—and fled to drown in a nearby lake. It was also the place where Connla the Fair, son of King Conn and brother of Art, was tempted into the other world by a woman of the Sídh. Despite the attempts of Conn's druids to defeat her, she threw the young Connla an apple, which placed an enchantment on him so that when she reappeared to him he sailed away with her, never again to be seen by his family. Eochaidh Ollathair, the horse god and consort of the goddess Áine, was also said to have a residence on Uisneach, and Geoffrey of Monmouth claimed that the stones of Stonehenge came from the hill, brought to England through the magic power of Merlin. Fintan the Sage had his home here.

Below: *Ancient Irish druids in traditional dress. The figure on the right is an arch-druid with gold chain, cap and wand.*

One of the strongest traditions, however, is that of the sacred fires of Uisneach, lit every Bealtaine or May Eve. The fires continued to be lit here long after St. Patrick had cursed the hill. A great gathering was held on the hill at the time and cattle were driven through the twin fires to protect them for the coming year. Large quantities of animal bones were also found during the excavations at Uisneach, indicating either great feasting or animal sacrifice, or perhaps both. There is a holy well further west along the road from the Catstone and a tradition says that there is a further, hidden well on the hillside. The *bile* or sacred ash tree of Uisneach was one of the four great trees of pagan Celtic Ireland. Thus the hill encompasses all of the traditional physical attributes of a sacred landscape—rock and water, tree and ritual fire.

I had a strange experience on the evening after my visit to Uisneach. After a very long day which had included a lot of driving, I was travelling from Cavan to Dublin, along a stretch of minor road which was totally unknown to me and which was, after a couple of wrong turns and missed signs, beginning to seem endless. It was a rainy dusk, but the sky was still streaked with light. The road wound its way through hedges, hills, trees, and fields, each part of the route seeming very like the one before. I found myself passing through a valley with sloping hills on either side—a valley that seemed very familiar. In my tiredness and disorientation, it seemed to me to be the same valley where I had stopped earlier to view the Catstone. For a crazy moment, I wondered if I had strayed so far from my route that I had found my way back to Uisneach; I even began to look out for the black and white cows I had noticed on the hill opposite earlier on. Then I passed a huge house built of raw red brick, which I knew I hadn't seen before, and the strange feeling passed. But it made me wonder if that was part of the secret of Uisneach's centrality—not just that the stone touches each of the provinces while owing allegiance to none, but that where it is located could be a place anywhere in Ireland—a green hill, with ditches and dikes and small blue flowers, with gorse and hawthorn growing over it; a place that in terms of political importance is "nowhere" but that is, in some sense, everywhere.

FINTAN THE SEER

Fintan the Seer was brought from his home at Uisneach before the king and nobles at Tara and they asked of him how the land should be governed and divided, for he was the oldest and wisest man in Ireland. They asked him first who he was, what his lineage was and how long he had lived.

He answered them: "I am the son of Labhraidh and Bóchna. When I was fifteen years of age, I came with Cessair and Buan and fifty women to this shore, at Bun Suaine in the south. That was forty days before the deluge, and I was the only one to survive the great rains, for I hid in a cave at the mountain of Tounthinna near the Shannon. When I came from that cave, I

Above:
The huge, cracked limestone boulder known as the Catstone, or the Stone of Divisions, on the Hill of Uisneach.

was the first man to see the new land with the waters gone. That is five thousand and five hundred years ago, and since then I have taken many forms. I have been the one-eyed salmon at the falls of Assaroe, and have given wisdom to those who came to me. I have talked to the hawk of Achill, who is nearly as old as myself, and heard many stories from him. I have been a falcon, flying high over the hills where Fionn and the Fianna hunted. I have been an eagle, watching the kings and queens at Tara come to greatness, and then dying, one after the other. I have seen forests grow up from seeds, and fall and become trackless bogs. I have seen generations cut the forests and build palaces and temples, and I have seen those houses crumble to the same dust as those who built them. I have seen the tribes invade, and conquer those who were here before them; I have seen them be defeated by new tribes in their turn. What all my years have taught me is that all living things change—the land, the water, the people. Even the great rocks crumble in time.

"I planted one of the five great trees of Ireland—the Ash of Uisneach—and I have watched it fall and grow again from its seeds. Because I have seen so many things, I know how the land should be divided and the ways that those who rule should disport themselves.

"Let me tell you this, and make a record of it, so that generations to come should know it. Let there be Knowledge in the West, Battle in the North, Prosperity in the East, Music in the South, Royalty at the Centre. The royal centre is not only here at Tara, but also at Uisneach, for at Uisneach is the Stone of Divisions that touches on every province of Ireland, and so partakes of all their virtues. Tara and Uisneach are like the two kidneys of a beast, of equal necessity for the health of the people and the land. Tara is great—it is the place of governance; but keep the knowledge of Uisneach and the harmony of the land will continue.

"Let it be recorded that a ruler should have no blemish on his spirit, for if he has, the land will fail and the people go hungry. Let there be justice rather than might in ruling the land, and no bloodshed or battles in the struggle to hold it. Treat the land as your mother, and it will continue to feed you. Treat it as a slave to be used, and it may rise up in revolt. Let the great ones keep in mind that every ruler who lives will die, and every race give way to a new one."

Thus spoke Fintan, the oldest and wisest one, as wise ones have spoken before and since. And the kings and the nobles and warriors seemed to listen, and his words were written down; though whether any of those who heard paid much heed to them is another matter entirely.

Glencree, Wicklow

GLEANN CRIOTHAIGH

Scholars have claimed both Glencree and Bohernabreena as the location of the famous "hostel"—*Bruiden Dá Derga*—where King Conaire met his death. The site was certainly somewhere in the Wicklow or Dublin mountains, as this was the route of the Slí Cualann, one of the great roads from Tara. Eugene O'Curry was the first to suggest Bohernabreena, as, according to the story, the hostel was built over the Dodder and the place name incorporates "*Brú*," or "hostel," and *Bóthar*, or "road." In 1935, Henry Morris made the case for Glencree as the site, with the hostel situated over Mareen's Brook, which flows into the headwaters of the Dodder, while Ferguson had previously suggested Donnybrook. Given this uncertainty about the location, I have decided to take Glencree as the most likely situation—it is certainly the most atmospheric of the suggested locations and a perfect gateway to the Wicklow mountains. Its name means "The Glen of the Marshy Place."

The county of Wicklow is the youngest in Ireland—it was established only in 1606 when it was "shired," in an attempt to rout out the Gaelic rebels who lived in the hills and constantly raided the south and west of the Dublin suburbs. Wicklow, with its high mountains, deep glens and dark forests, was bandit country—the home of the rebel, the fugitive and the hermit. It was also a place of escape from the city of Dublin, and so it continues to this day; with its bogs and heather-covered hills, its isolation and its beauty. Much of the county is now preserved as a natural park, with woodland walks and trails through unspoilt countryside. The great woods of Wicklow have been replanted and it is now one of the most forested areas in Ireland—although there is some concern that the mechanical planting and logging may have an adverse effect on the native wildlife and the archaeological remains of the county. Most of these prehistoric remains are situated in the gentler hills and valleys to the northwest of the county, towards the Kildare border. The wilder land of the high mountain ranges has always been less hospitable for settlement, which is why rebellion continued to be fomented here as late as the beginning of the nineteenth century. Glencree was so heavily wooded

Below:
The Wicklow mountains.

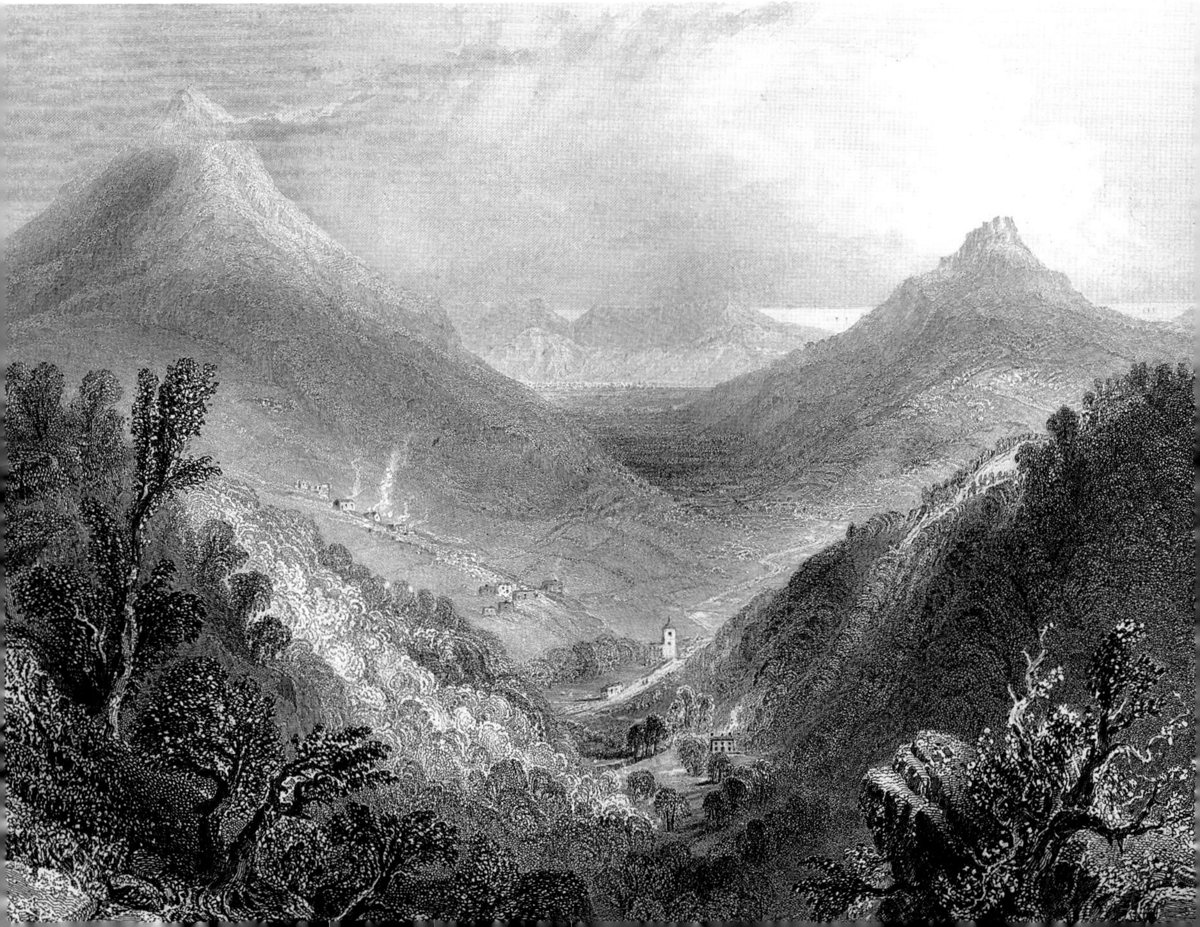

in medieval times that it was made a Royal Deer Park and enclosed in the thirteenth century, but by Tudor times it had fallen back to wildness, and a concentrated effort had been made to clear its forests so that they could not act as cover for the wood kerne, the Irish rebel soldiers. Later, the military road was built over the mountains—the same route which still links Glencree with Aughavannagh. At the same time, a barracks was built in the valley at Glencree—a building which later became a boys' reformatory. Glencree is also the site of a burial ground for German airmen who crashed in Ireland during World War II, and an iron cross marks the site where the body of a young republican was left by his killers during Ireland's Civil War. When swirling mists part to allow the strange conical top of Knockree, the Hill of the King, to be seen, the presence of the dead in this valley can feel more powerful than that of the living. In nearby Glenasmole, the lovely valley of thrushes, Oisín, the son of Fionn, fell from his horse on his return from the Land of Youth.

The young king, Conaire, felled by the swords of his foster-brothers and their allies; Oisín, falling from his horse; airmen, falling from the sky; men and trees falling before the axe—these are dark stories for such a lovely place. But the Wicklow mountains are equally famous for another exile from society who came to these isolated glens in search of a different kind of refuge. St. Kevin was a saint who loved wild things far more than humans. It was said that once he stood still for so long that a blackbird laid her eggs in his hand and he waited in that position until the young birds were hatched. After he had founded the great monastery of Glendalough, he grew tired of the crowds who followed him there, and made his way over the mountains to another lonely valley, north of Glencree—a place that is now known as Hollywood Glen. Here, he refused to cut any timber, either to clear his way or to build a shelter, and when he came to the great forest, the trees, out of love for him, moved aside and made a path for him through the wood.

DA DEARGA'S HOSTEL

Frost and ice covered the mountains from the glens of Dún Bolg to the sea. It was a hard, cold, black night with no lights showing in the vastness of the high moors of the mountains by Áth Cliath. A band of warriors travelled through the pitch darkness, guided only by the stars, for the moon was still no more than a faint bow in the sky, and it seemed reddish—soiled with blood. At their head was Conaire, the young, fair-haired king of Ireland. Despite his great youth and the fact that he had not been bred as a king but in exile, until very recently his reign had been one of plenty—poets said that from Bealtaine until Samhain, no wind strong enough to stir a cow's tail disturbed the peace of the land. He was a kindly king, with sleepy grey eyes and an air of seriousness about him despite his youth. They said that his father had been a bird spirit of the Sídh, who had come to his mother in secret and lain with her. His mother, Mes Buachalla, was the granddaughter of the fair Étaín, the most beautiful woman in Ireland. Though Étaín had been taken into the mounds of the Sídh long ago, the poets still used her beauty as the ultimate standard of loveliness in women; and those who looked at Conaire saw that beauty take the form of a man.

However, recently, things had changed. It was said that the king had broken the *geasa*, the solemn prohibitions that had been put upon him at his coming to the kingship. Strange signs had been seen in the sky; crops had failed; and winter—a winter so bitterly cold that it froze every river and lake in Ireland—had set in. And, most ominous of all, ships had started to land on the east coast, coming from Britain and full of sea pirates. Incgel, the British marauder, had joined with Conaire's foster-brothers, who had been sent into exile for their raping and raiding in Ireland. It was said that they were joining with others who did not want to see Conaire's peaceful reign continue—for in times of peace, there is little loot for those who love war.

Conaire was now seeking shelter with an old friend and companion, Da Dearga, the Red One—the most generous host in the land. The king was weak and weary, but knew that he had to keep near the ocean to defend his land against the threat from the east. He already felt a sense of doom, for earlier that day, when they had been climbing steadily from the coast in the red glow of sunset, three riders had swept past them. At first, Conaire had thought that it was the sun that turned them to the colour of flame, but then he realised that everything about them was red—their hair, their skin, their clothes, their horses. He remembered yet another of his *geasa*—"Do not let the Three Reds go before you to the house of the Red One."

Conaire sent a messenger to try to catch the horsemen and ask them to wait so that he could go ahead. The messenger had offered great gifts in exchange, but they had answered:

"We are the sons of Donn, riding the horses of Donn. Though we are alive, we are dead. There shall be much feasting this night in the house of the one of the dark face; many shall come to partake of his feast. We ride together. The three red ones stop for no one, neither king nor peasant." And they spurred on their horses and rode even faster, westwards towards the hostel of Da Dearga.

Above: *Grotto at Glencree.*

The march continued, interrupted only by the calling of the wolves in the hills. A strange pair passed the troop—a man and a woman, one more ugly and twisted than the other, and the man with a pig on his back, a pig that was half-roasted but still alive and squealing. Finally, they reached the hill where the hostel stood. Lights blazed from the window, for Da Dearga always welcomed travellers weary of the bleak terrain around his home. Mac Cécht, the king's closest companion, looked fearfully at Conaire, for was that not yet another of the *geasa*—that his king should never spend the night in a dwelling where light showed outside the walls? But Conaire's usually cheerful face was sunk into his cloak, and his grey eyes were dark. Da Dearga welcomed the company nobly, providing food and drink and warm fires, and they cheered a little as they sat by the glowing hearth. However, soon there was another interruption—a black, twisted woman, demanding entrance, though it was well after sunset. They brought her before Conaire, who asked her name. "Cailb," she said.

"That is a short name," said Conaire.

"I am also called Sind, and Sinann and many other names." And the woman began to give such a list of names—many of them people of the Sídh—that Conaire raised his hand to stop her.

"And what is it that you want?" he asked.

"A night's lodging, with the king's company, which you will agree is not much to ask."

"I would give you anything but that, woman," said Conaire. "But it is my *geis* not to allow a visiting woman into my dwelling after sunset. Instead, let me send you good food and drink and a fire outside."

"Is that the way the king treats a poor old woman?" asked the hag indignantly. "Indeed, it is a fine state Ireland has got into with a ruler like that."

She continued to berate him in this vein, so that finally Conaire sighed and said, "Very well, come in then and stay."

So was the last of his *geasa* broken. But as the servants led the crone away, she turned to Conaire and said, in a voice loud and clear for one so old and bent, "No flesh of yours shall escape this place you have come to—save what the birds carry away on their claws. Many will take the long drink of death this night in Da Dearga's hall."

The evening seemed long. Although the company was weary, they sat up together by the fires, fearful of the darkness outside; fearful also of attack from the east. Sometimes the wind rose up, and the company stirred, thinking of warriors creeping over the gorse of the hills; sometimes wolves called. Conaire remembered when he had last visited Da Dearga, when the hostel had been filled with the sound of birdsong and singing streams—a heavenly place in summer, full of life. Now all was death and stillness and frozen air.

While the king sat, he pondered on what had led him to this cold place in the hills. Was it the malice of the Sídh or his own weakness in allowing his foster-brothers to live? But why should the Sídh bear him malice, for surely he had done nothing against them? Conaire had never been told of the story of his mother and grandmother, the two Étaíns; and so he was powerless to understand the malice the Sídh bore him because of his grandfather's crimes. It seemed to him that every *geis* he had broken had been unavoidable, through a wish to do good. He thought of his child, now being carried under Mac Cécht's arm; of his sweet wife, who would surely mourn him and just as surely be courted and marry again. He had been touched with fate from the day he had followed the white speckled birds to the strand near Áth Cliath, and one had changed into human form and warned him against killing any of his father's people, the bird spirits. If he could fly now, he thought, he could leave all this behind him—the misery of his tribe, the threat of the raiders. But he knew that even if he could fly, he would not do so, for he was a king, and a king remained with his people. He stirred restlessly. Why could he not get over the feeling that he was being watched, that there were spies peering in the windows of the lighted *dún*?

The wolves called louder and Conaire remembered that his foster-brothers had taken werewolves into their company. There was a sudden crashing on the doors of the house, and streams of warriors burst through, each one armed with a long, cruel spear of iron, each one as vicious as a wolf on the mountainside. As they entered, they set fire to the house, so that their swords were lit with a red glow and the walls flamed the colour of blood. The company sprang to arms, and the battle began. It is said that Conaire killed six hundred there, and would have killed many more, perhaps even routed the invaders, had it not been for the spells that the magicians of the enemy cast upon him. He was overcome with a great thirst, so that he sank to the ground in agony.

"Who will bring me a drink this night?" he called piteously.

Mac Cécht stood nearby, trying to comfort him and keep the attacking warriors away from his side. He looked around, frantic for a servant to send for water, but all were either dead or fled into the dark hills. He raced outwards into the darkness, but the stream next to the house was bound with frost; all that flowed from the house was red blood. Then he raced, with the speed of desperation, to every lake and river in Ireland, trying to fill his master's drinking cup, but all their life-giving water was frozen under a coat of solid ice. Finally, in a sheltered valley, he found ice that he could break, and, having filled the cup with water, he raced back to the hostel.

A red dawn was rising over the hall, and, at the door, two men were savagely hacking the head from Conaire's body. All around lay bodies, the crows beginning to battle over their flesh. Mac Cécht fought the two attackers—the last stand of the invading hordes—and killed them, though his arm was hacked off and his body gashed to ribbons with their spears. He took the cup to where the head of his master was, the grey eyes still open, the lips cracked and dry as is if still gasping for the water. He lifted the cup to Conaire's lips and they sucked in the water thirstily. Then the head spoke: "Mac Cécht, my dear one, my flower of warriors, I would be generous to you in my gratitude, were I still living."

The eyes closed, and Mac Cécht collapsed.

When the sun was high in the sky, a woman of the valley crept from her cave in the hills to see what had happened, for all seemed quiet now at the battlefield. She came upon the severed head of Conaire, and the mighty warrior lying beside it. A she-wolf was tearing at the flesh of the warrior, but ran off whimpering when the woman threw a well-aimed stone at her. She brought Mac Cécht some of the water from the cup that was beside him, and then went to fetch more water from the stream, for it seemed that the cold spell was over and the ice was beginning to melt.

As she wiped his brow, he awoke with a jolt and reached for his sword.

She laid her hand gently on his arm.

"Stop now—there has been enough killing; so many warriors dead. Do you know that there was a wolf up to her shoulders in the wound in your side?" she asked.

He shook his head dumbly. She wondered if his wits had left him in the carnage surrounding them.

"Who are you?" she asked.

His voice came out, dry like old leaves rustling together, not that of the young man he seemed to be. "I am Mac Cécht, one of the warriors of Conaire, the sweetest and most just king ever to rule."

He tried to struggle upwards, then fell back, in agony.

"Let me take the king back with me to Tara, where he may lie with the bones of his ancestors, for never did a man deserve less the enmity of the Sídh or of mankind. Truly, tonight many have drunk the drink of death at this hostel."

The reason for the Sídh's revenge on Conaire can be read in "The Finding of Étaín."

St. Mullins, Carlow

TEACH MOLAING

Unlike most of the sites which were visited during the writing of this book, the tiny village of St. Mullins was visited at a time when it was full of people. Every year, on the Sunday before St. James's Day (July 25), a mass is held in the ancient graveyard on the site, attended by people from the local community. Flowers are brought to the graves of the families of the dead, and St. Moling's Well is visited. It is a family day out with representatives of every generation, from new-born babies to men and women in their nineties. The atmosphere, even within the graveyard, is a holiday one. Travellers set up stalls, and picnics are held on the banks of the river; groups of people perch themselves on the edge of graves, chatting quietly with everyone who passes.

The natural setting for this community event is a particularly lovely one. St. Mullins is situated not far from New Ross, on the banks of the River Barrow, with Mount Brandon to the northwest and the Blackstairs mountains to the northeast. The river is wide and amber brown here; St. Mullins is the point where it stops being tidal. The banks of the river are heavily forested and the ancient remains of

the monastic settlement nestle between small hills and old trees. There is hardly any village as such, but there are the ruins of a round tower and a number of churches, a holy well dedicated to St. Moling, the site of Moling's mill, a Norman motte and interesting old mill buildings at the edge of the river. It is a popular place with fishermen, particularly in May when the shad come upriver.

Above:
St. Mullin's Church, County Carlow.

The pattern held in July is a very ancient one, stemming from the blessing that Moling gave to the waters of the river and its tributary. For thirteen centuries, pilgrims have travelled the leafy green lanes to come to this place of sanctuary and healing. During the Black Death in 1348, hundreds came here to wade in the water and pray to be saved from the disease. It is more than likely that this place was sacred even before the time of Moling, who lived in the seventh century; it is recorded under the name of *Ross Bruic* or Badger Wood in the Fianna stories. Moling himself is one of the most attractive figures of all the ancient Irish saints. He seems to have been a transition figure between the pagan and Christian world, for as well as offering sanctuary to Suibhne, he had the famous craftsman, the Gobán Saor (probably a variation on the great god of smithcraft, Goibhniu) build his sanctuary. It is said that he used the Great Yew of Ross, one of the noble trees of Ireland, as his roof. Moling introduced the milling of rye to the locality, digging the watercourse for his mill with his own hands, and acted as a ferryman for those needing to cross the river. He also had a very close relationship with the natural world—he tamed wild dogs, spoke to foxes and birds and was particularly lacking in the vindictiveness displayed by many of the early Irish saints. He was a gentle saint, happy to live in the great woods that fringed the river. Like the mad king, Suibhne, to whom he gave comfort, he was a wonderful leaper, able to move through the treetops as if they were his second home.

The themes the local priest talked about at the St. Mullins pattern were close to the spirit of the stories of Moling—healing for the soul and sanctuary for those wounded by life. There were hundreds of people gathered among the forest of tombstones in the graveyard and many more scattered in the surrounding hills, but everyone was influenced by the peacefulness of the place. Small children chased each other up and down the motte and groups of teenagers congregated at the riverside, but they did so quietly. It may be that Moling's serene spirit lives on.

THE DEATH OF SUIBHNE

It was a pleasant afternoon in mid-July. The wood was alive with the calling of small birds, and sometimes, far in the distance, the baying of a hound. Green light filtered through the heavy canopy of leaves on the banks of the broad and peaceful river, and Muirgil the cowherd's wife was humming as she worked. She was happy, though a little preoccupied; she had hardly seemed to notice when her husband, Mongán, had left to go about his tasks, his face even more thundery than usual. Mongán was a jealous man, rarely at peace in his mind. Muirgil had known that from the beginning. His jealousy was one of the reasons why they were living in this quiet clearing in the forest, with only the holy man Moling for company—for who could be jealous of a saint? Soon Muirgil would tell him her pleasant news, for she could no longer keep it to herself, and she knew that her husband had found her distant, absent-minded and wrapped up in her own thoughts this past while. But she had wanted to be sure—she was not going to let that sister of Mongán's, who was always trying to make trouble between them, have the chance to say that she was boasting without cause. However, she decided that this evening she would break the news to him. Surely his jealousy and discontent would leave him when he discovered that she was to have his child.

She squinted against the light that broke through a clearing in the forest—a tall woman was coming along the track. She was dressed in a dark blue robe, and even from a distance, Muirgil admired the fine quality of the cloth from which it was made. As she came closer, Muirgil noticed that the woman's hair was the colour of iron and her face was lined with care, but there was still great beauty there. Her bearing was stately and she was obviously a great lady. Muirgil thought it strange that she should have come so far into the forest alone. The cowherd's wife moved forward to welcome her, for hospitality was one of the laws by which their tiny community lived.

After they had exchanged greetings, the woman said, "I am Eorann, wife of Suibhne, the king of Dál Riada, long lost to madness in the forest. I have heard that he has come to these woods. Have you seen him?"

Muirgil smiled. "Ah, that is why you have come—to find our poor man of the wood. Yes, I have seen Suibhne, but just glimpses, for he is as shy as any forest creature. I pour milk for him every day at sunset and he comes just to the boundary of the house to drink it. Every day, he flies all over Ireland, leaping from tree to tree like a bird or a squirrel. But every evening he comes back to this clearing and spends the night here, listening to the words of the holy hermit. I have never spoken to him nor touched him for he will let no one but the holy Moling come near him. But he has told his story to the saint, of his years of madness, living in the trees and flying and leaping from branch to branch. And you are his wife?"

Eorann nodded sadly. "I was once, but he has repudiated me. It is a long story. Would you mind if I sat with you awhile?"

Muirgil brought her into the shade and gave her milk and bread, and honey from their own bees. Then, turning to her, she asked her to tell her the tale of Suibhne.

Eorann began: "My husband, Suibhne, was always a hasty man, and on many occasions I have had to stop him before he acted unwisely. But a braver or kinder husband you could never find. I loved him dearly, and bore him a daughter and a son. Then—and I do not know how it happened—during the great battle of Moira, he lost his mind. The priests have told me that it was because he insulted the cleric Rónán—my husband never cared for Christian ways—but I have always thought that it was the battle itself that sent him mad: the noise, the destruction, the smell. It was a dreadful, bloody fight; the crows gathered over the corpses for days afterwards, feasting on their flesh. In any case, his friend, Loingseachán, told me that in the middle of it all, Suibhne began to scream and to whirl around in circles, and the next minute he had leapt into the highest branches of a yew tree.

"He would not come down, even after the battle was over and the corpses had been carried away; it was as if he no longer wanted to have anything to do with humans. I went to try to call to him down, but he only leapt away, going west towards Donegal. For months, he lived by jumping from tree to tree, his feet never touching the ground, his hair unkempt and his clothes gone to rags. His sweet mouth was stained with the herbs and grasses he lived on.

"In the end, Loingseachán tricked him into coming down out of the trees and he came home to me. But he was changed. He told me that he no longer wanted to be king; that he could not stay or settle in one place, even for a night, for the sights and screams of the battle were always with him and movement was the only way to get away from his visions of the horror. I begged him to let me go with him, saying that I would rather live in rags and in cold and hunger with him than with rich jewels in a palace without him; but the madness overtook him again, and he left me one night, travelling far to the woody glens south of our home. I consulted with Loingseachán, and we agreed another trick to try to get him home again—telling him that his family was dead. He fell to the ground in grief and was caught and carried to his palace but, once again, the madness overtook him. He saw phantoms, he said, in his dreams, screaming and crying and fighting with one another. The horrors would wake him in the night, and even when he was with me and I held him as tightly as I could, it made no difference—he bucked and screamed in my arms like a wild thing. So it went on like this. He left me

Opposite:
St. Moling's Well, where the annual pattern commences every year on the Sunday before St. James's Day.

again; then he came back to me again, but by that time I was with someone else. He berated me, but as I said to him, what was a woman to do? He had his mad friends in the forest; he had the company of wild things and the joy of the green crown of trees around him; I had nothing to hold me but the arms of a man. And so he went away again, and I cried long and hard, but I swore that it would be for the last time.

"I was in bed one night when he came to the tree outside my window, and made a poem. That poem was the loveliest thing that I have ever heard. He sang of the forest—the clear springs so full of fish-life, the call of the thrushes and the other wild things, the belling of the great stags in winter. It made me weep to hear him, but the poem made me realise that he was lost to me forever, lost to the forest and the world of the wild woods and the trees and the birds. He could no more come back to being a human king than I could fly through the trees with him. So I rose up and went to him and said, 'You are back now, but I know you will go again. You cannot stay in the company of other humans; now your companions are the creatures of the wild. So, as I know that all it will take is a clear night or the call of the north wind to make you leave me, I ask you to leave me now. Go, and do not come back.'

"That was the hardest thing I ever had to say. There was silence from the hazel tree outside my window, and then his voice came again—oh, his sweet voice: "I will be gone then. Let me tell you: the cry of the grouse on the mountainside is in any case far sweeter to me than the voice of my wife lying beside me."

The woman paused and looked down at her hands.

"That is the last time I have seen him or heard his voice. I have wept every night since then; and all I want to know now is that he is safe and has found some peace in his poor head."

Muirgil took her hands gently. Although this woman was a queen, Muirgil felt nothing but compassion for her grief and a sense of her own wealth and happiness in comparison.

"I think," she said, "that holy Moling may have given him some kind of rest. I think that he has found refuge and healing here in this place of trees and water." She paused and looked over towards the wood.

"Look," she said. "The shadows are lengthening. He will come soon for his milk. Would you like to try to talk to him when he comes?"

Eorann shook her head. "No, I do not want to speak to him or let him know that I am here. But if I were to stand in the shadow of the hut, I could perhaps see him when he comes."

Muirgil filled a pail with warm milk and went to the edge of the forest. She thought that she saw something move in the shadows to the west. Then she saw Suibhne, running in from another part of the forest. The birds sang softly. She smiled her sweetest smile, encouraging him to come closer. Perhaps it was that smile that brought her husband, watching from the shadowy trees, over the brink into his own madness.

There was a flash of steel in the slant of the sun, and a cry. Suibhne fell, his body pierced by the spear of Mongán. Mongán's sister had told him that his wife loved the man of the woods, and now, driven to frenzy by the thought that his wife had slept with the mad king, he had killed him. Mongán stood in the shadows, staring at his hands. Muirgil dropped the pitcher and ran to where the king had fallen, calling out for St. Moling to come and help her. The blue-robed woman moved out from the shelter of the hut and walked slowly towards her husband's body as the light died over the western woods.

MUNSTER

Lough Muskry, Tipperary

LOCH BÉAL SÉAD

The Glen of Aherlow with its surrounding mountains is an area of Tipperary which deserves to be better known. The banks of the River Aherlow are beautifully forested and steeped in history, while the walks on the mountains to hidden lakes and panoramic views are the equal of any in Ireland. Lough Muskry is one such hidden lake, situated high in the mountains and not accessible by car. The walk to the lake and back should take no more than three hours from where the road ends in the forestry south of Rossadrehid village. The walk is quite steep but is not overly difficult, as there is a trail for the full extent of it, and the views of the surrounding mountains and of the lake itself make it more than worthwhile. Much of the early part of the route is through planted forest, with the latter part moving onto open moorland. One of the best times to undertake the walk is in the very early morning, when on sunny days you will have the experience of seeing the thick white mist clear from the river valley below, leaving bright blue skies and magnificent views of the glen. While the lake itself is not visible from the track, it is easy to identify the rim of the corrie in which it lies. The towering cliffs which surround the lake form a natural amphitheatre, the rocks gouged as if slashed by a knife. The water of the lake is dark and very cold looking, and there is little bird life around it. However warm the day, one is unlikely to be tempted to cool off in its green depths. To the north is Knockastakeen, where the strange rock formation, the *Fir Bréaga* or "False Men" stands out clearly.

Pages 80–81: *"The Lower and Torc Lakes, Killarney," engraving by W.H. Bartlett.*

The lake was formerly known as *Lough Béal Séad*—the Lake of the Jewel Mouth—but it has also been identified as Loch Béal Dragan, the lake of the Dragon's Mouth. Its present name, Lough Muskry, comes from the Múscraighe sept who lived in the south of Ireland. The lake is said to have been formed on the spot where Cliach the harper stood for a year to serenade his beloved, the daughter of Bodhbh of Slievenamon. The tradition continues that a *piast*, or serpent, emerges from the lake on stormy nights. Another local tradition has it that if a special grass grown near the lake is eaten, it will cure scurvy. This tradition has been upheld by botanical studies of the lakeside which have shown that scurvy grass is present in the area. Material collected by the Folklore Commission in the 1930s demonstrates the range of legends attached to the area of the Glen of Aherlow and the Galtee Mountains. This manuscript collection contains stories of buried treasures (often

Above:
On the mountain path to Lough Muskry, County Tipperary.

"Danish gold"); of holy wells moving location because they had been ill-treated by a user; of houses being left undisturbed after their owners died because the living did not wish to disturb the dead; of festive Lughnasa journeys into the hills to collect bilberries, on the last Sunday of July. Further back in time, William Le Fanu, the brother of the celebrated writer, Sheridan, walked across the Galtees in 1838. A fog came down and, for a time, the members of the party were completely lost, wandering in the mist and unable to get their bearings. They finally found shelter but when they mentioned that in their travels they had seen a chestnut horse running alone across the hills, they were told that they were lucky to have come back alive. The "yellow horse," they were told, was a fairy steed, which usually foreshadowed the death of those who had seen it.

We saw no fairy steeds on our trip; nor were there any swans with golden collars gliding on the lake. But on a warm May morning, the walk to Lough Muskry was idyllic. Stonechats darted and squabbled at the side of the track, and lambs, white enough to act as advertisements for washing powder, scrambled across the path and down the rocks, plaintively calling for their mothers. The valleys stretched away into a blue haze, and the larks that sang seemed to celebrate the return of the sun and the beginning of summer—at least for a day.

THE VISION OF AONGHUS

Aonghus, the child of youth and the god of love and beauty, lay sick in his bed in the Brú, and no one could say what ailed him. He fell in and out of a sleep that seemed to do him no good, for he moaned and called out while he slept, and awoke weeping. The people of the Sídh began to fear that he would never recover and dreaded the darkness that such a fate would bring to them.

For it was Aonghus who protected lovers everywhere, who came with the spring with his bright cloud of singing birds. Yet still he would not say what ailed him, but only begged to be left alone so that he could sleep.

Finally, after a year, his mother, Bóinn, the goddess of the great river Boyne, became desperate. She sent for one of the greatest and wisest of the druids. He came to where Aonghus lay on his bronze bed and took one look at him. Then he said, "Easy it is to see what ails the lad."

The court waited expectantly.

"He is in love, and his beloved appears to him while he sleeps. He will never be well until he finds out who this girl that he is dreaming about is and gets her as his wife."

Aonghus raised a pale head from the pillow and smiled. "In truth," he said, "I did not know my sickness until you told me of it. But so it is: the most beautiful girl in the world has visited me in my dreams and sings to me in the night. I will never be well until I find her. She has cheeks the colour of the yew berry and hair the colour of the dark night. Her eyes are bright lakes and her neck is white as a swan. She will not let me touch her; when I try to grasp her in my arms I wake up. Tell me how I may find her."

The druid replied: "You must seek her all over Ireland; for she, like you, is one of the Sídh, and she must love you, for why else would she come to you when you sleep?"

For many months, Aonghus's mother and his father—the great Daghdha himself—searched for the maiden with whom Aonghus had fallen in love. Their search grew more frantic as the months went on and the youth grew paler and weaker, and the flowers faded early in the fields, and the birds were silent on bare branches. Finally, they spoke to Bodhbh, the great otherworld king of Munster, who had his *sídh* in Slievenamon. He told them of a girl who was as fair as Aonghus's vision. She was Caer Iobharmhéith, the sweet yew-berry, the daughter of Ethal Anbhuail of the Munster Sídh. She had been sent by her father to live at Crotta Cliach in the Galtee mountains, by the lake known as Loch Béal Dragan, a high, hidden lake in the wild mountains. The girl was under an enchantment; she went in the form of a girl and a swan in alternate years, and she was the only one who could choose which form she took. To find her, Aonghus must go to the lake on the next Samhain eve.

At the beginning of November, Bodhbh and Aonghus travelled from the Brú over bogs and river-valleys, wide plains and high, silent mountains. It was not until they had reached the edge of the lake that they could see it at all, for it was hidden in a cup in the hills. As they climbed the last slope, Aonghus listened intently, hoping to hear the sound of his beloved's voice. But all was still and silent. Gliding over the surface of the dark waters of the lake was a multitude of shining white birds; fifty of them were attached to one another by chains of silver; but one, the most beautiful and graceful of them all, had a chain of gold.

Aonghus stood at the lakeshore, saying nothing. He did not see the shape that had enchanted him in his dreams; he saw only white swans. How could he be sure that his beloved was here? How could he know her? Standing beside him, Bodhbh said nothing. Aonghus reached out to catch the swan with the golden collar, but she flew away from him, across the water. The evening was darkening and the moon rose over the black lake.

Then the silence of the mountains was broken by Aonghus's voice, calling the girl to him, telling her of his love. Aonghus sang of how he had dreamed of Caer for many long months, of how his life was worth nothing without her by his side.

"Come to me!" he sang. "Whatever form you take, I will cleave to you; wherever you go, I will follow. I will not oppose your will, whether you be swan or maiden; if you come to me on land, I will not hinder you from going again into the water. Only come to me now!"

And so, finally, she came, breaking the chain that bound her to her handmaidens. As the white bird set her foot on dry land, Aonghus saw that she was indeed the girl with eyes full of light who had come to him in his dreams. And at the moment of recognition, there was a further transformation. Aonghus himself stepped forward into the dark water, and in that moment he too changed; he became a great white bird, a swan to be a swan's mate. He and the girl embraced and, as swans, took flight over the water. They circled the lake three times, and then, linked together by the golden chain, they flew northwards, over the moonlit mountains towards Brú na Bóinne. As they flew, they sang a song of such beauty and joy that all who heard it fell into a deep sleep. The inhabitants of Ireland, Sídh and human, slept for three days and three nights and had such dreams that their lives were transformed when they awoke, each one finding a world made new, full of enchantment. Caer was the wife of Aonghus from that day on, and, as part of his bridal gift, Aonghus gave her four kisses, which he forged into singing birds.

Slievenamon, Tipperary

SLIABH NA mBAN

Slievenamon (*Sliabh na mBan*, "The Mound of the Women," or *Sídh Femen*, "The *Sídh* of the Women"), a mountain bordering Tipperary and Kilkenny, was one of the most important *sídh*, or otherworld residences, in Irish tradition. Nowadays, the nineteenth-century song, "Slievenamon," is still sung, having acquired the status of a local anthem. The mountain dominates the surrounding landscape and there is a clearly defined track to the cairn near its summit. The small village of Kilcash nestling on the slopes of the mountain is a pretty, sleepy place with a Romanesque church and a ruined Butler castle nearby. There are magnificent views from the summit, although the mountain has long been cleared of its original forests. The early nineteenth-century "Lament for Kilcash" mourns not only Lady Margaret Butler, but also this lost world, where the great woods symbolised a past nobility:

What shall we do now for timber?
The last of the woods is down.
Kilcash and the house of its glory
And the bell of the house are gone.

—"Caoine Cill Chais," anonymous translation Frank O'Connor

The cairn on the mountain is the traditional home of Bodhbh Dearg, one of the great otherworld lords, who was given this *sídh* when Manannán divided the underground palaces between the Tuatha Dé Danann after they had been defeated by the Milesians and driven into the mounds. The Fianna hunted here, and in the forests that covered the mountain they must often have held their rituals. This was the mountain on which Fionn and his companions finally stopped after their wild chase from Tory in the north, hunting a magical deer. On Slievenamon, snow surrounded the Fianna and they found themselves inside the fairy mound, guests of the Lord Donn, who asked for their help in a battle against other members of the Tuatha Dé Danann. Here also lived Cnú Dearóil, the marvellous musician only four fingers high who played music that could break the hearts of listeners. From here too, according to the ancient text, *Agallamh na Senórach*, came another musician, Cos Corach—perhaps Cnú in another form—whom St. Patrick blessed for the beauty of his music. It was to here

that Midhir, one of the Tuatha Dé Danann, fleeing from King Eochaidh, brought his beloved and long-sought-after Étaín, before the couple made their way to Midhir's *sídh* at Brí Léith in Longford.

Yet another tradition says that Slievenamon was named "The Mound of the Women" (*Sliabh na mBan*) because a great troop of women raced to the top to gain the prize of Fionn as a husband. In some accounts, Fionn was given his magical powers on Slievenamon, when he followed a beautiful woman and caught his thumb in the doorway as she disappeared into a *sídh*. From that time on, when he put the thumb into his mouth, he could see far into the distance in space and time. The tradition of fairy women associated with the hill survived well into the last century. In the story of the fairy spinners, for example, a woman's cottage is invaded by the Sídh; but she runs in screaming that Slievenamon is on fire, and the fairy women leave in a great rush to save their homes. However, there have been darker manifestations of belief in magic than the common folk motifs of mysterious lights appearing on the mountain or fairy troops seen crossing a traveller's path late at night. As late as 1902, William Murphy was brought to court for trying to bewitch his neighbour's cows on May 1. There is also the story of Bridget Cleary, a young woman from the village of Cloneen in the foothills of the mountain, who in 1895 was burnt to death by her husband, Michael Cleary, in an attempt to drive away the fairy being he thought was possessing her. The case made headlines at the time and children sang a rhyme for many years afterwards: "Are you a witch or are you a fairy/Or are you the wife of Michael Cleary?"

In general, the music of Slievenamon is not so harsh. Listen to it. It is there in the memory of the deep humming of the Fianna ritual trances, a chanting that is echoed in the buzzing of the bees in the heather. It is there in the soft accents of the local people, in the sighing of the breeze and the songs of the hidden birds in the trees around the ruined walls of Kilcash. It is heard late at night in the villages under the mountain, when local musicians come in to play tunes which seem to have their roots in other worlds.

THE BIRTH OF OISÍN

The slopes of Slievenamon are known to be enchanted, but whether this enchantment comes from the presence of the great *sídh* of Ard Femen or

from the beauty of its forest of hazel and alder, of slender birch and copper beech, cannot be said. Whatever the reason, of all the places in Ireland where broad-faced young Fionn loved to hunt, the slopes of Slievenamon were among the most beloved.

It was a spring dawn, a cold one with a fresh wind—on such mornings, Fionn loved to begin his hunts, watching the deer flee before him through the bright green branches, almost always sure of capturing them with the help of his hounds, Bran and Sceolan. The woods were still wet with dew when suddenly, from a thicket, a doe started out and the hounds began a tremendous baying. The fawn—as white as milk or freshly fallen snow—raced through the branches, but before it did so it cast a glance back at Fionn, the only person near enough to see it clearly. The look made him stop in his tracks, for it was not that of a frightened animal but of a human being, pleading and proud at the same time. He shook the thought off and followed his hounds to where they ran close on the heels of the fawn. They ran through glades of hazel and oak, and as the day wore on, and Fionn and the hounds still followed the deer, they left the forest and went further and further up the slopes of Slievenamon, into a high silent valley that Fionn had never seen before. There, having left the rest of the hunt far behind, the doe suddenly stopped dead in her tracks and lay down quietly by the edge of a stream. "They have her now!" thought Fionn exultantly; but instead of attacking the fawn, the two dogs put their ears down and cowered before her, whimpering, as if half-afraid and half-delighted. When Fionn came up to her, he raised his spear; but when he looked into those deep and liquid brown eyes, he slowly put it down. For the first time in his life, Fionn found that he could not kill.

So, instead, he put his hand gently on the doe's head and she nuzzled it, licking it with a soft, pink tongue.

"You must be a beast of the Sídh," said Fionn.

When the rest of his companions joined him, Fionn ordered that no harm should come to the doe, but that they should bring it back to Almiu, his great palace at the Hill of Allen in Kildare.

That night, all but one of the deer was roasted on the great fires of Almiu. The Fianna feasted and sang and told stories and Fionn went late to bed. He had not lain there long when he heard someone entering his room. He immediately reached for his sword, but put it down when he heard a gentle laugh and he saw that what was before him was not a warrior but a beautiful young girl. Her skin was as white as milk or newly fallen snow; her hair was as dark as midnight; her eyes brown, as gentle as a deer's.

"Who are you?" he asked gently. "And why do you laugh?"

Below:
The castle ruins at Kilcash, County Tipperary.

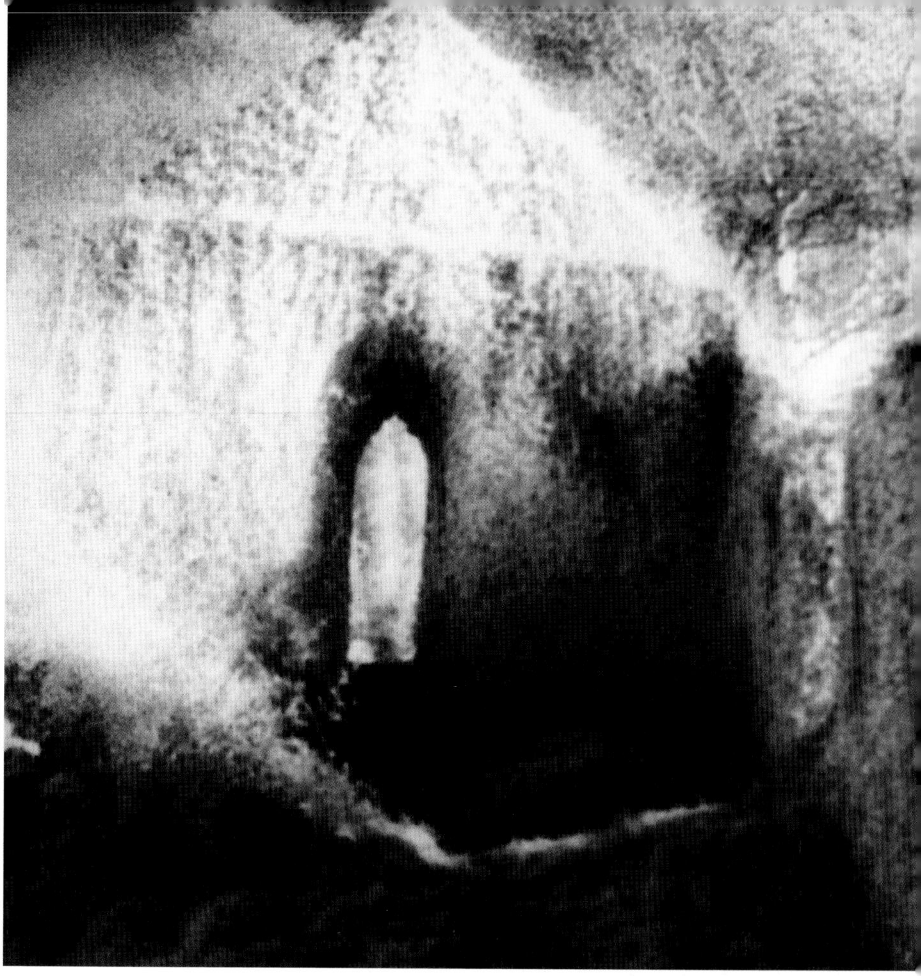

"I am laughing," said the maiden, "because I have finally found my heart's desire, and I was afraid I might be killed by him, though death at his hand would be preferable to life at the hand of another. And who I am is Sadhbh, called also Bláí Dearg, for my father is the magician Dearg, who does not love you, and therefore would not let me come to you. I had no lover in the people of the Sídh, but one wanted me, the Fear Dorcha, and that Dark Man has pursued me night and day in my form as a doe. Will you give me your protection, for I have looked for you for a long time to ask you to do so?"

"I will not just give you my protection," said Fionn, drawing the bedclothes aside. "I will give you my love and make you my wife."

Fionn loved Sadhbh with all the passion of his young and passionate nature. He could hardly bear to be from her side for a moment, so when the day came when he had to go to battle against his ancient enemies, he found it difficult to drag himself away.

"I will look out for you from the ramparts of Almiu," said Sadhbh. "And as soon as I see you coming, I will run out and greet you."

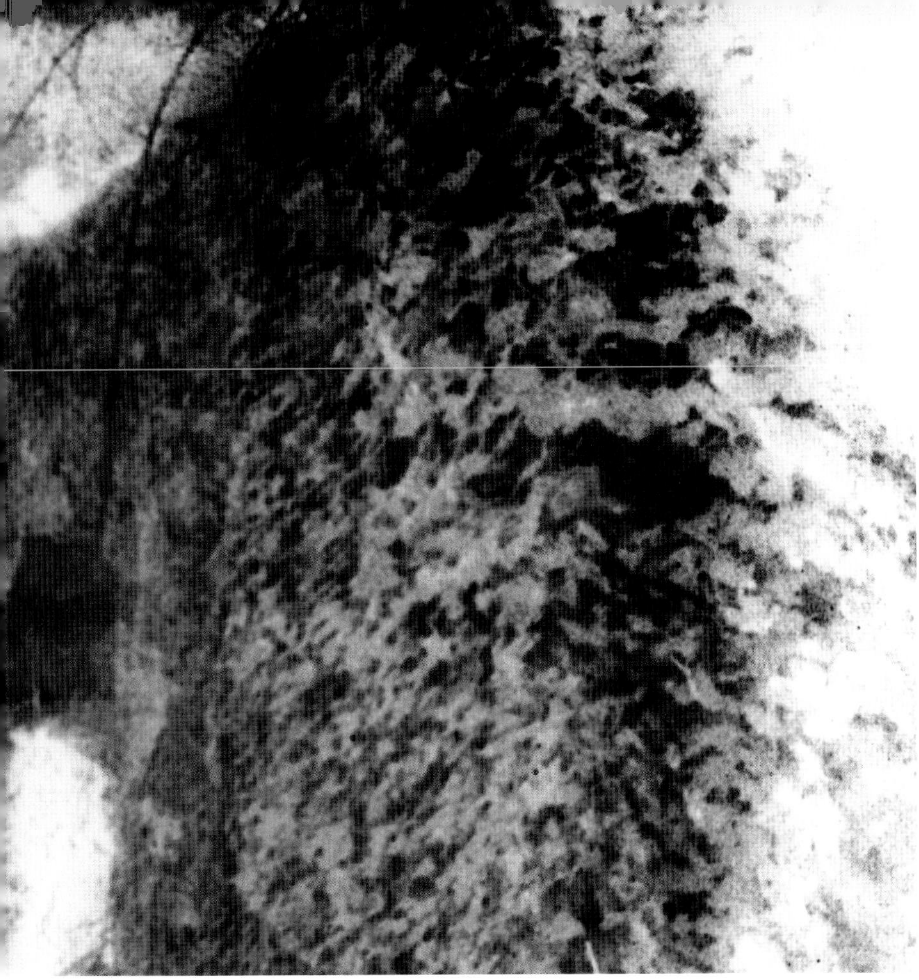

Left:
Ruined church, Kilcash.

"Do not run too fast, my love," said Fionn, laying his hand gently on her stomach. "For I do not want you to harm the child."

However, when Fionn returned victorious from battle, he found no one running to meet him. The *dún* was in chaos, with servants running to and fro, calling each other names and trying to shift the blame from one to another. Finally, he managed to get some sense from his steward: "My lady is gone," he said, stuttering over the words. "She was up on the *dún*. She was watching eastwards from where she knew you would come, And then it seemed as if someone with your countenance and bearing appeared, with two great hounds by his side. Before we could stop her, she had run out towards you, her arms outstretched, and you know yourself, my lord, how fleet of foot she is—none of us could catch her. But as soon as she drew near to the man, it seemed that his appearance changed to that of a dark man in a black cloak, and the dogs with him were not Bran and Sceolan, but two great dark hounds who came towards my lady and dragged her by her gown to where he stood; and then ..." The servant paused, looking fearfully at his master.

"Well, and then what?"

"Then he raised his rod—it seemed to be of hazel or some such wood—and touched her. And in the place of our lady there was a doe, which tried to run towards the *dún*. But every hound in the place set up such a howling and barking and strained to get at her, and the dark man's hounds pulled and nipped at her, so that she was forced to go with him. He led her away into a mist that suddenly came down, though it had been a bright day before that. We have not seen her since, but we have sent our people far and wide, looking for some trace of her. It is as if the ground had swallowed her."

Fionn said nothing. He went to his own room and lay on his bed, which still held a faint woodland scent on the sheets. He knew that it was the Fear Dorcha who had found his wife and taken her away.

For the next five years, Fionn hunted like a man possessed—every glen and forest in Ireland rang to the calls of Bran and Sceolan; every hillside echoed with his halloos. Whether it was deep winter or high summer, Fionn hunted—not for the shy, brown deer or the angry boar to feed the bellies of his men, but for his lost beloved. As time went on, hope faded, and Fionn became older and colder and he took other women to his bed, but he never forgot his sweet, early love.

Then, one day in early spring, when the Fianna were hunting on Ben Bulben, a mist came down, separating Fionn from the rest of his band. Only Sceolan and Bran and their three pups, who were bidding to become as great dogs as their dams, were with him. They ran ahead of Fionn into a narrow valley that reminded him of somewhere, though he was sure he had never been there before. As he made his way carefully along, the mist began to clear a little, and he could see the five dogs standing in a circle and baying joyously. They moved apart so that he could see what they were guarding, and there in the centre of the group was a small boy. The child had skin like milk or newly fallen snow, and long dark eyes, as liquid and gentle as Sadhbh's. But the boy's golden hair was the colour of Fionn's and his nose and jaw had the set, even at four years of age, of that hero. There was a tiny tuft of soft, brown hair on his forehead—the shape that might be left from the gentle lick of a doe. Fionn, although he would never find Sadhbh again, had been given his son, who would become a poet and one of the great ones of the Fianna. He named him Oisín, which means Little Deer.

BÉARA

Béara Peninsula, Cork

This is a landscape without compromise, especially in winter—a landscape of jumbled rocks, grey and white and black. On the summits, the rocks are striated, as if scratched with a witch's claws. The fields are full of russet ferns, copper reeds, and grass the colour of blood that has been dry for a very long time. This wild and mountainous region is entered through gateways which are deceptively fertile and gentle—Glengarriff, full of tropical plants and heavily planted with trees, so that in the misty rain, the twisted pines and rocky islands look like something in a Japanese print; or on the other side of the peninsula, Kenmare, folded into its mountains and straddling the lovely Kenmare River. However, beyond each of these places is the Béara Peninsula, home of the *Cailleach Bhéarra* (Hag of Béara)—glorious in summer, but perhaps most itself during the cold days of winter. The hard rocks—the bones of the land—are revealed under buffeting wind and driving rain; and the presence of the sea, both preserver and destroyer of the people who have settled here for thousands of years, is a constant, angry presence in our ears.

The people of the past are remembered in the rich folklore of the region. There are the stories of the Gaibhleann Gabha, the mythical smith—an appropriate presence in an area which was once rich in copper and silver, and has a tradition of mining going back centuries. The name Béara is traditionally said to come from the name of a Spanish princess, who married a local chieftain, but no single character is more associated with the peninsula than the Cailleach or Hag of Béara. This ambivalent character is likely to be a surviving form of an ancient land-goddess and the ritual consort of human kings. The imagery associated with her is sombre. Sometimes she is said to be the wife of Manannán Mac Lir, god of the sea, but she is also connected in the stories with the lord of death, Donn, and she appears in various forms all over Ireland. In some areas, she was associated with the harvest, so that the last sheaf cut was known as the *cailleach*. In Scotland, she was the protector of wild animals. On the Béara peninsula, she is associated most strongly with the cow, and it is possible that her original name, *Boí* or *Buí* comes from the old word for cow. Dunboy and Inis Boí—an ancient name for Dursey—hold echoes of that connection, as do the rocks beyond Dursey—the Bull, the Cow and the Calf. The Bull Rock is one of those places known as the House of Donn, the palace in the west where the lord of death called the dying to him.

Bere Island, a short ferry ride from Castletown Bere, the main town on the peninsula, was inhabited from early prehistoric times. It has a wealth of antiquities—wedge tombs, ringforts, holy wells, standing stones and promontory forts. Indeed, the whole peninsula is covered with the remnants of very ancient times, and at Ballycrovane, on the northwestern side of the peninsula, you can find the tallest ogham stone in Ireland, set against a magnificent backdrop of small islands on one side and great mountains on the other. The Ring of Béara corkscrews through these mountains, each one more dramatic than the last, and then opens out into views of sea and rock and silver light. The more sheltered valleys are miracles of green, and the two-storey traditional farmhouses that they hold sometimes seem to be suspended, swimming in the rivers of mist which surround them, or perched like nests on impossibly rocky heights. Not far away from Ballycrovane, at Coulagh, a rock jutting out from a cliffside is known as the Cailleach. She faces into the sea and wind, turned to stone by St. Catherine because of a dispute over a prayer book. As you approach from the road, the rock does indeed seem like the shape of an old, hook-nosed woman, her body half submerged in the earth. Offerings of coins are still left here.

Just outside Castletown Bere, with its busy port, its pubs, its restaurants and its industries, there lies another such place where centuries seem to meet and mingle. Dunboy, the site of Dónal Cam O'Sullivan's castle, is now a lonely ruin, facing out into the sea. Defeated by the English forces under Carew, the last chief of Dunboy set out from there on the last day of 1601 to make the long journey northwards to Leitrim, where he hoped to find refuge and allies. One thousand men, women and children accompanied him on that harsh winter journey. Out of that number, thirty-five survived to reach Leitrim. Inland from the shell of the castle lies another ruin, that of a glorious nineteenth-century mansion burnt to the ground during the War of Independence. In Dunboy's small harbour, the wind plays through the bare ribs of a boat, long ago wrecked and left to be stripped by the elements. And perhaps the Cailleach looks on, remembering old battles lost, and white bones that have been picked as clean as the wrecked vessel, to become part of her skeletal landscape.

THE HAG OF BÉARA

Cold darkness. Even in the pain and the panic, the thought came into his head: "So this is death." He had often wondered about death, although he had seen little of it, for he was a prince and he had led a sheltered life. A dog of his had died—a small red dog killed by his father when she became too old even to take comfort in lying by the fire or taking scraps of meat from his hand. His father had said, "She is better off so; she was only suffering." But he had not believed him. Surely life was always better than death.

So now he fought for his life, struggling against the black waves and the wild wind, calling out for help, though no one sailed this stretch of water between the island of Béara and the mainland, haunted as it was with tales of hags and witches. And then the blackness overcame him.

"Once I slept with princes, stronger and wealthier and far, far fairer than you. But that was long ago."

The old woman stirred the fire and the young man huddled closer to it. The cabin smelled of damp and old age, of drying seaweed and sulky turf. The fire gave little heat, and the boy shivered. After unconsciousness had come upon him as his body sank deep into the waves, he could remember nothing. He had woken to find himself in this hovel, being fed a thin green soup that seemed to be mostly dirt-coloured water with a few strands of cress floating in it. Yet, although the soup made his stomach churn, at least it was hot, and he was alive. The boy peered at the crone opposite him. He could hardly distinguish a face behind the acrid smoke that filled the cabin and the grey veil that the hag wore. He wondered how her rheumy eyes could see beyond the thick cloth at all, and shivered slightly as he remembered stories of the Hag of Béara, the Cailleach who could just as easily kill a man as rescue him.

The woman cackled as she caught him staring.

"You do not know who I am? Am I no longer known by the men of Ireland? I have had many names. Once my names were almost as beautiful as I was myself. I was called Boí, the Cow-woman, and I had herds of fine beasts grazing all over this peninsula. I could fly through the air over the mountains; I could run in a hare's shape through the golden cornfields; and I drank mead and wine with the great kings. I had so many lovers they could not be counted; to each one I was as generous with my body as I was with my treasure. I had fifty foster-children whom I raised to greatness. One of my greatest lovers was Fothadh Canainne, that mighty warrior. He feasted only when there were dead men present at the table, and his head still spoke to me after it had been taken from his body by treachery. How he loved my long, golden hair—you see now, there is not much left, and what there is is grey and thin."

She pulled a strand of greasy hair out from behind the veil. The young man said nothing, for he could think of nothing to say. The woman cackled again, as if amused at his discomfort.

"It is as well that I wear a veil in these days. The tide is ebbing now—can you hear it call? Now, there is greed in men's hearts rather than valiant deeds, meanness and treachery instead of hospitality and courage. There is no nobleness left in this land. You do not know what it was like, in the days of the kings when the gods walked with us, and any moment we could be visited by one of the great lords—by Aonghus or Donn or the great Daghdha himself. In those days, any woman could be the mother of a god, and any man the lover of

Above:
A standing stone on Bere Island keeps watch over the Atlantic Ocean.

a woman of the Sídh. If you had seen me dressed in the richest of cloth, with white gold at my ears and my neck, and yellow gold plaited in shining balls through my hair! If you had seen that beauty, you would not easily forget it. We feasted, we made music, we made love. Great races; great battles; many, many gifts given by the great kings and queens. And the deeds—the feats of gods and heroes. Gods cleared mountains and forests and built great fortresses; men would as soon die as lose their honour or break their word. No one now has the courage of greatness, of a generous spirit. I look now, and I see the tide turn back in, come back again in its full flow, though it seemed weakened and gone forever. But I know that I will never be the same again, will never come back from my ebbing into strength and beauty. I see the plains covered each year with golden grain; but I know that the gold will never come back to my hair. Those who once lay in my arms now row over the ford at Alma, over and over again, rowing through the rushes, rowing in a bitter cold place, towards the house of Donn, towards the house of death. But death is the one thing that has not been granted to me. You were almost dead, child, when I took you from the water. I could have given you death, but I would rather you lived and know the misery of age. Do not look at me with such pity in your eyes; I am not so blind yet that I cannot see it. You think you understand what I am saying? Of the body fading, greying, weakening, the sight going, even my teeth rotten so that the least of the pleasures I once knew is gone? Of the arms no longer firm and white, but grey and wrinkled?"

The prince started to protest, to promise the comfort of rewards from his father and mother for saving his life, to speak of his sorrow for her pain—but the figure opposite refused to let him speak.

"You do not believe you will ever be old—yes, you know it in your mind, but every part of your body denies it."

The hag rose, and to the young man she seemed no longer an old, decrepit woman, but a creature powerful and frightening, filled with anger.

"Get you gone now, with your big, dark eyes and your calf's stare; get out of my sight for I have said too much. You have seen too much, for you have seen the Cailleach. Remember her words when your body betrays you with age. But go, go from her. There is a boat out there on the beach. The storm is over and the ebb tide will bring you back to your land."

And as he made a gesture of gratitude towards her, she pushed him away and spat her parting words at him:

"Do not thank me. Do not try to take my hand. I am not to be touched. Leave me, now; and do not try to come back."

Killarney, Kerry

CILL ÁIRNE

By any standards, the district surrounding the Lakes of Killarney is incredibly beautiful. Killarney (*Cill Áirne*, "Church of the Sloe") is situated in County Kerry, between the Macgillicuddy Reeks and the Mangerton Mountains, close to the influence of the warm Gulf Stream, which results in a landscape that contains a wide variety of luxuriant vegetation. The particular combination of the high, rugged mountains (the highest in Ireland), the three lakes, the woodland and the many islands dotting the lakes makes the district one of stupendous natural beauty. Up until the early nineteenth century, this was a wild and isolated spot—the haunt of highwaymen, some of whom are still remembered in the names of the caves where they hid in the mountains. The area has suffered, however, more than any part of Ireland from a feeling of tourist overkill—the lakes have left the kingdom of Kerry and entered the kingdom of cliché. During the nineteenth century,

Above:
W.H. Bartlett's nineteenth-century engraving depicting the "Approach to Killarney from the Kenmare Road."
Opposite:
"The Torc Cascade," County Kerry, engraving by W.H. Bartlett.

everybody who was anybody visited the lakes, and usually wrote about them, for they saw in this place the epitome of a romantic landscape. Wordsworth and Tennyson, Thackeray and those indefatigable travellers, the Halls, Charlotte Brontë (who came here on her honeymoon), even Queen Victoria—they came, they saw, and they rhapsodised with various degrees of romantic hyperbole. The pattern continued into the twentieth century, when the area became a Mecca for transatlantic visitors. There was an exponential growth of tourist attractions such as Kate Kearney's cottage and the Colleen Bawn's rock—all to be visited by jaunting car, if possible.

The legend of Oisín, which is associated with Lough Leane, is the most recent in this book, although it stems from a much older tradition which has Oisín returning to Ireland after hundreds of years. He had many long conversations with St. Patrick, in which they discussed the relative values of the old, wild, heroic days and the new, gentler order; and it must be said that his case for the old world view often makes it seem the more attractive time. Oisín is commemorated in the road which runs down the Iveragh Peninsula, which is signposted as Bealach Oisín.

Killarney itself is a pleasant enough town, though there is a palpable feeling of a place that feeds on tourism. The establishment of a National Park has at least had the result of preventing the expansion of hotels and restaurants in the most beautiful areas around the lakes, and it is still possible, with a little effort, to strip away the Disneyland associations and connect with the place as it must have been before the tourist invasion of the last two centuries.

Such a place is sometimes wild and terrible, especially when the storms that are a regular feature of such a mountainous region lash down on the rocks and whip the waters of the lakes into a black frenzy. However, it can also seem to be the most serene place on the planet, in early morning when the still water of the lakes is glimpsed through the ancient oak woodlands. There are three main lakes in Killarney—the Upper Lake, the smallest of the three, high in the mountains near the gap of Dunloe; the Middle Lake or Muckross Lake, on the banks of which stands the impressive Muckross Abbey and a useful information centre; and the largest of the three, Lough Leane or the Lower Lake, nearest the town itself and dotted with thirty islands. Lough Leane is said to be named after a retainer of the god Bodhbh from Slievenamon who was called Len Linfiaclach.

It is possible to take a boat trip on the lakes and visit some of the islands. Many of these are covered with semi-tropical vegetation, such as bamboo and eucalyptus. In June, the colours of the rhododendron are stunning. The plant is not a native one but has flourished so wildly in the warm temperate climate of the south of Ireland that, despite its beauty, it is now considered a pest and a threat to native species. On Inisfallen island there are the ruins of an abbey, reputedly founded by St. Finian the Leper, where the Annals of Innisfallen—a seminal source of early Irish history—were written between the eleventh and thirteenth centuries. Other areas of exceptional beauty include the Torc waterfall and the gap of Dunloe to the south of Lough Leane. It is worthwhile to make the effort to get away from the more popular sites, where hordes of tourists are disgorged from the maws of coaches. If you are very lucky, in the high upland areas, you may see one of the herds of the red deer, a species which has roamed the Irish countryside for thousands of years. Alternatively, choose a wet day for your trip, preferably with an odd roll of thunder and flash of lightning thrown in. Most of the crowds will have taken refuge inside the restaurants and you will be able enter into the wildness of the place. And if the mountains are not as visible as you might like, you may lose yourself instead in the wet, green world of the ancient woodlands. In this world, if you hear a clattering of horse's hooves in the distance, it will be easier to imagine that this is not yet another jaunting car, carrying a shivering tourist desperate for the sight of a thatched cottage which serves cappuccino, but rather the horse of a woman of the Sídh, coming from the other side of the mist in search of her human lover.

THE RETURN OF OISÍN

I am fallen here, in this Wicklow glen, like a dead leaf on the floor of the forest. I am the dried husk of summer, waiting to be crushed into the earth, unable to move without the help of those who, a moment ago, thought me some kind of god. They look down at me, horrified; one minute they were seeing a fine warrior on a white horse, the next minute an ancient withered man, transformed as soon as I touched the soil of Ireland. The people's faces are coarse and cowardly, their limbs puny; I have seen no one here that has a quarter of the strength or nobility of my companions of old. But every one of them is stronger than me now.

Yet the summer is as sweet as it ever was, though the noise of the forest is torture to me now, in this woody glen, so full of life. Full of sap rising, birds building, bees humming, linnets, thrushes and ringdoves. All is flowering, all is alive and full to bursting. And the bells of the Christian priests tell me over and over again that my world has gone.

It was in another such beautiful glen, in autumn, that I hunted with my father, Fionn Mac Cumhaill, and my son, Oscar, near Loch Leane in the south. In autumn, that place has the saddest beauty, the beauty of a world about to change. It was a clear, cold morning that we started out.

"Oisín," my father called out. "You take your company down by the lake. I think there are the tracks of a young fawn down there."

I nodded, although I resented my father telling me how to go about the hunt. I knew I still had things to learn from him about woodcraft and magic, but he was no longer the man he had once been; bitter lines had been etched on his mouth since Diarmaid's betrayal of him and his of Diarmaid. Lines were on his forehead from the long battle with his old companion, Goll. Yet still I felt as if I walked in his shadow. But as I made my way down towards the lakeside, I forgot him in my joy in the beauty of the mountains and the water and the excitement of the hunt.

Then I stopped, for riding towards me over the hillside was the most beautiful woman I had ever seen. Her skin was whiter than a white rose. Her hair was the gold of the sun, her eyes the colour of a thrush's egg. She rode a fine white horse, with golden reins and saddle, and as she came towards me, I could see that her eyes were shining with joy.

"I have found you at last," she said as she approached me. "Oisín, I have sought you long, and come so far to find you, for I have seen you in dreams and I know that you are my heart's match."

Opposite:
Killarney woods.

I could say nothing. I, Oisín, the great poet and teller of tales, was struck dumb by her loveliness.

"Will you come with me?" she asked sweetly. "I am Niamh, Princess of the Golden Hair, and I have come from the Land of Pleasure to take you back there with me as my husband. Will you come with me?"

I was so overtaken with desire for this lovely woman that had she asked me to go with her anywhere in this world or any other, I would have left without a backwards look. I saw nothing, neither my father nor my son coming up behind me, calling me. I went to her, and she pulled me onto her horse. We rode like the wind away from that place, leaving my companions calling behind me. The journey took us over seas and plains and mountains, and far beyond the land of Ireland; finally, we reached her father's place. They treated me with great honour there and I lived with my sweet bride for what seemed to me to be three years, and had a son and a daughter by her. I lived a life of pleasure—of hunting and feasting and laughter. But one day I awoke with a longing in my heart to see my companions again, and my son Oscar and the fair land of Ireland, and even my father; for I thought that now I should no longer feel that I lived in his shadow, having lived so long in the bright sunlight of the other world. I imagined the stories I would have to tell them, how they would listen to me in wonder. So finally I went to Niamh and said, "My sweetheart, you know I love you better than life itself, but I feel that I must visit my family and my companions. Will you come with me that you may be welcomed by my people as I have been welcomed by yours?"

Niamh's hands fell from her needlework.

"Oisín," she said. "Let me ask you not to do this. I cannot come with you and I fear that you will not return if you leave me to visit Ireland."

"My love," I said firmly. "Nothing would keep me away from you. If you will not come with me, let me go alone. I will return before you know that I have gone."

My wife nodded. "So the day I dreaded has come. So be it, then. But take the white horse we rode on to come here; and promise me one thing—that you will not dismount from his back no matter what happens. Promise me that, if nothing else."

I laughed a little—so this was her trick to make sure that my visit was a short one! But she looked so disconsolate that I promised what she wished.

The white horse carried me like the wind to Ireland; but it was not the Ireland of my youth. It seemed as if a race of dwarfs—ugly, misshapen weaklings—had taken over the island. I rode through the valleys asking the people for news of Fionn and the Fianna, but no one seemed to know what I was talking about. Everyone looked blank, except for one very old man who said that he had heard stories of such heroes who had dwelt in the forests three hundred years before. Slowly, I began to realise that what had passed for a year in the Land of the Young was a hundred years in the world of mortals; my father, my child and my companions had long since become white bones, rotted into the land itself.

Yet still I rode through the countryside, for although the people had changed, the land remained familiar, and I hoped to find the traces of my lost world. Finally, I came here to Gleann na Smól, the valley of thrushes, where I met a group of men trying to shift a heavy boulder. They begged me to help them, for like the rest of the inhabitants they were a puny lot. I leaned from the back of the white horse to shift the stone, and as I did so, a bell rang out from a neighbouring valley and the horse bolted, throwing me to the ground. As soon as I touched earth, I felt my flesh wither, my eyes fade, my strength seep from me. Within seconds, I was an ancient heap of skin and bones, and the white horse had galloped off, back to the fair princess I would never see again.

Always, those who leave expect to come back to the same world. They want it to be unchanged—the same companions opening their arms to welcome them; the girls they left years before as young and pretty as ever; their friends gathered together, agog to hear stories of adventure. But those who leave never come back to the same place. Indeed, now I sometimes wonder if that lost world really existed—if my memory has recreated it in brighter colours than the ones it actually held. When I tell these people of how the world was when I was young, I can see that they only half-believe me. They smile behind their hands to see me weep, but I will weep my fill, because Fionn and the Fianna are no longer living. They look at my withered flesh and offer to bring me to the man who is preaching of a new god. His name is Patrick and he talks of something called the soul and promises eternal life.

I do not want eternal life. I would sell what the Christians call my soul to have only one day of my youth again—to be alive and strong and a part of the green world, to hear the hounds baying in the forest, the sweet note of the blackbird, and my companions calling me to the hunt.

Caherconree, Kerry

CATHAIR CHONROÍ

The Slieve Mish mountains act as the barrier to an area that has one of the richest local heritages—in terms of archaeological remains, language, folklore and music—in the island of Ireland. The Dingle Peninsula, or *Corca Dhuibhne* (named for one of the septs who lived here in ancient times), is also one of the most astoundingly beautiful places in the country and, as a result of this, has become something of a tourist fly-trap in recent years. However, within a few miles of where a United Nations of visitors eat in restaurants with cuisine (and prices) comparable to the capitals of Europe, there are high and lonely green valleys, cloud-covered for much of the year, where the old ways have not changed greatly and the feeling remains of another world.

One such valley is that of the Finglas River, which leads to the base of Slieve Mish and is one of the starting points for the approach to Caherconree hill-fort. The fort is situated on a spur of Baurtregaum mountain, 683 metres (2,241 feet) above sea level. The climb to the fort is not an easy one, and should be attempted only in good weather—the best route to take is to turn off from the Castlemaine Road to the south where the ascent is marked by red and white poles, a route which avoids the worst of the bogs. At the fort, the views are magnificent, incorporating much of west Munster. Be aware, however, that the mists can come down suddenly and surround you completely, leaving you imprisoned in a grey, swirling world of stone and water-laden air. The hill-fort, which has not been dated exactly but was certainly in use by the Celtic Iron Age, is what is known as an inland promontory fort, with cliffs falling steeply to the north, south and west, and a 110-metre (360-foot) line of massive sandstone blocks stretching fully across the mountain spur and acting as the defence to the east. It was thus almost impregnable—with no entrance apart from the two gateways in the line of rocks.

The location of the fort indicates that it acted as a defence or marker between two tribes; it still forms the boundary between the baronies of Corkaguiney and Trughanacny. There are the remains of a number of stone huts inside the walls and there was also originally a stone trough which was removed in the nineteenth century. However, little else remains to give evidence of the life within the fort. Historically, Caherconree was said to have had seven battles fought around it, but

Below:
Muckross Abbey, County Kerry, by A. Nicholl.

probably, because of its situation, had completely fallen out of use by the time of the Normans. By the nineteenth century, there was even some dispute as to whether anything remained of the legendary *cathair*. For the legends endured—Caherconree was still famous as the stone fort of the great warrior magician, Cú Roí, from which its name comes.

Cú Roí is an important figure in the stories of the Ulster Cycle, acting as a wise judge and arbitrator in some of its tales. It was he who judged who should receive the champion's portion. He did this by fighting the three great heroes of the Red Branch—Cónal, Laoghaire and Cú Chulainn—in the form of a demon outside his fortress. He eventually awarded the prize to Cú Chulainn, though their relationship was to sour badly in later years. Cú Roí seems to have been associated with the sun. He was said to be a great traveller who returned to his fortress in the evening. He could make the fortress revolve, and so no one could gain entrance to his shining, spinning palace after sunset. But when he was angry he could become terrible. When he helped the men of Ulster in their raid on Iuchar's fortress and he was not included in the sharing of the spoils, he took a terrible revenge.

In legendary terms, the Slieve Mish mountains are also associated with the coming to Ireland of the sons of Míl. They landed at Kenmare Bay on Bealtaine (May) eve and fought their first battle with the Tuatha Dé Danann here. Scota, their queen and wife of Míl, died in the battle and was buried at the place known as Scota's Grave near Tralee. Another Milesian princess, Fas, is buried in nearby Glen Fais. On Slieve Mish, the Milesians met Banba, one of the three queens of Ireland after whom the island was named. As well as having a wealth of legends associated with it, the area is also exceptionally rich in the physical remains of the past—in the early 1980s, an archaeological survey, carried out on the Corca Dhuibhne area, listed no fewer than 1,572 sites of interest. These included rock art, tombs, standing stones, cairns, ring-barrows, promontory forts, ogham stones, holy wells and a large number of wedge tombs dating from the Bronze Age, when the district as a whole seems to have experienced a population explosion.

The slopes and valleys around the Slieve Mish mountains are thinly inhabited today, and the isolation of these valleys may be one of the reasons for their association with madness—Glanagalt (*Gleann na nGealt*, "The Glen of the Mad People"), the valley where it was reputed that all the insane people of Ireland (including Suibhne or Mad Sweeney) felt compelled to visit, is a little to the west, and Mis herself, after whom the mountain range is named, was said to be a princess who was driven to insanity by the death of her father in battle. When the mist comes down and the valleys become as isolated as islands, it is easy to understand these associations.

If the mist and rain do come down, and Cú Roí's fortress refuses to show itself, spend time around the village of Camp and in the Finglas valley. Finnghlas, the white speckled river, is known as such because of the milk poured down by Cú Roí's wife, Bláthnaid, as a sign to her lover that the time had come to rescue her from her prison in the clouds. The river winds its way through woods of oak and holly, the dark greenness broken only by the vivid colours of montbretia and fuchsia—a world away from the high bleak beauty of the mountainside.

THE DEATH OF CÚ ROÍ

A clear day on the mountain, and a girl with nut-brown hair was carrying a bucket of milk in from where three white cows were pastured. The birds that played about the cows circled her head, unafraid, for the cows were Iuchar's, and Bláthnaid, the flower-like one, was the daughter of that same king. A tall man in a dark grey cloak came down towards her.

"Leave it, my love. Let one of the servants do that."

The girl smiled, and said in a voice as soft as music, "Are not all the servants down helping out with building the palace that you are making for me, the greatest palace in Ireland? Are not all the men at arms and bondmaids and builders working down there, and the harpers along with them to keep them cheerful? Are we not the only ones left up here on the mountain?"

Cú Roí, the great king and even greater magician, laughed. His face was like that of a blazing lion, though his curling mane had long ago turned as grey as his cloak.

"Indeed they are—they are all doing your bidding, sweet one. All but Feircheirdne, who is going to play music for us; his tunes are too good to labour to. Let us lie in the sun and listen to him. Ah, here he is. Feircheirdne, play for us."

Feircheirdne was a fair-haired man with grey eyes that were soft only when he played his music, or sometimes, but even then rarely, when he looked at his king.

"I have a new song, King," he said. "I have made it in honour of Bláthnaid, your new wife. It tells the story of how the men of Ulster would not share their spoils with you after you had helped them in their raid against Iuchar, king of the Isle of Man. It tells of how you took Bláthnaid and Iuchar's three cows and the magical cauldron away from the men of Ulster. It tells how you defeated that beardless youth, Cú Chulainn, the young pup they call the Hound of Ulster, and shaved his head and daubed his skull with dung when

Above: *The Slieve Mish mountains, County Kerry.*

he tried to fight you and steal her back from you. They say that he is still skulking around, ashamed to show his face until his hair grows again. It is a mighty song."

"She is not so new a wife, for it is nearly a year now that I have her," said Cú Roí fondly. "But she is all the dearer for that, for a sweeter girl was never born. She it is who calls me back here from all my wanderings. She is the one who holds all the secrets of my heart."

Bláthnaid put her hand on her husband's arm and said something softly into his ear. Cú Roí's ruddy face became redder and he smiled.

"Well, Feircheirdne, it seems that my wife would like to be alone with me today. Take the chariot out and go down to see how the work is progressing at the fortress."

Feircheirdne looked as if he might be about to protest, but he caught the glint in his master's eye and turned away, giving a peremptory bow to the lady. Bláthnaid drew her husband to the steps of the fort, where they could look down into the valley, blue and hazy on this summer's afternoon, the sea glinting in the distance no bluer than the girl's eyes.

"Let me look for lice in your head, beloved," she said. "I saw you scratching yesterday."

Cú Roí lay with his head in the girl's lap, content in his power and in his love for this captive princess. It seemed that the gentle hands wove their own spell over his grey curls, and she sang gently to him so that he almost slept. In his daze, he did not notice that men were gathering in the glen below Caherconree.

When the sun had risen to its highest point, Bláthnaid said, "Let me go and heat water for your bath. I will wash you and clean your hair, and then we will lie down together and take some rest."

"Can we not rest now?" said Cú Roí. Bláthnaid laughed. "No, let you wash yourself first, you old goat. Go inside and I will bring water."

Should anyone have been watching Bláthnaid when she went to the stream, they would have seen that she did a curious thing. She took two buckets with her, and while she filled one bucket with water, she poured the contents of the other into the spring. The milk from the marvellous cows coloured the water white as it mixed with the stream. She watched as it flowed downwards to the green valley—that place full of oak trees and holly and small flowers, so different from this cloudy palace where for most of the year she lived in a world enclosed by mist, a thick, grey mist that made her a captive of Cú Roí as effectively as bars and padlocks. Her father's small island had been like the valley, low-lying and fertile, not a fortress of hard, grey stone, of freezing, swirling fog and angry sunsets.

Back with Cú Roí, she washed him and, still singing to him, began to comb and play with his long locks as he lay on their bed. He felt something tug at his scalp and realised that his hair had been tied to the posts and bedrails.

He laughed. "What are you at, girl? What game is this? Leave over and come in beside me." He reached for her, but she was already behind the bed, tying another of his locks to the other bedrail.

"I told you, girl," he said, impatient now. "Leave that over." He reached out to try to untie the knots but they were tied so securely that he could not move. Then he saw his wife standing over him. His hands were grasped and bound; then his sword was in her hand, and a look in her hooded blue eyes that he had never seen before.

"I would kill you now, Bellowing Hound, myself with my own hand, only that I have promised that pleasure to Cú Chulainn for the shame you put on him. Old dog, know that you will die here today, with your servants far away, your home taken over by the men of the north; and with all your great powers you can do nothing about it, for you have been tricked by a girl. I sent milk down the stream to give the signal for Cú Chulainn and his men to attack, and I can hear them now at the open gate."

Cú Roí looked at her, still too confused to be angry. "But I thought you had grown to love me. Have I not given you everything you wanted?"

The girl laughed. "What did I want but the kisses of a young man and the freedom to be a princess in my own land? How could I love a man who stole me from my people, and raped me? How could I feel anything but horror and disgust at you, you hairy old goat of the mountains, who has put me in prison here in this grey place?"

At this moment, a bevy of warriors swept into the room, and though Cú Roí had no weapon but his teeth and his manacled fists, he killed a hundred of them before he succumbed. Cú Chulainn was the one who finally struck the blow that severed his head from his body.

The Hound of Ulster came to Bláthnaid where she stood looking out over the ramparts at Caherconree, towards the people returning to the *dún*. The day had clouded over, and the mist was filling the valley below, hiding the bright river and the fields where sheep grazed. She ran to the young hero and embraced him.

"Oh, my love," she said. "At last I am free of that old man."

There was a scuffle as Feircheirdne, the musician of Cú Roí, was brought before them, his arms held by the Ulster champions. He spat at Bláthnaid, glaring at her with fiery eyes.

"You bitch," he said. "I see you have chosen the young Hound of Ulster rather that the great Hound of Munster for your bed."

"Kill him," said Bláthnaid, turning from him.

Cú Chulainn shook his head. "He is a musician, not a warrior, and therefore worthy of protection," he said. "But do not dare speak to this lady in that way again," he added. "For she is to be my wife."

Feircheirdne laughed and with a mighty effort shook himself loose of the restraining hands. "Is she indeed? Well, maybe not all the plans you made together will come to pass."

He rushed towards where Bláthnaid stood, gazing out from the high walls of the *dún* over the rocky cliffside, and, catching her up in his arms, he jumped onto the rampart. He hesitated a second. No one knew whether he intended what happened next, or whether Bláthnaid's struggles caused it, but the two of them fell headlong into the mist, down onto the rocks below.

The three cows of Iuchar set up a mournful bellowing and the birds that circled their heads dropped to the ground, stricken to death. Cú Chulainn stood, gazing not at the two bodies lying twisted and broken far below, but at the bloody head of Cú Roí set up on a stake in the centre of the *dún*. It seemed to him that the face peering through the grey locks matted with blood smiled a lion's smile.

Knockainey, Limerick

CNOC ÁINE

The tiny village of Knockainey is located deep in the fertile county of Limerick, close to the great Megalithic complex of Lough Gur. This is the heartland of the lady Áine, the kindly goddess whose name originally meant "brightness." In the legends, the small hill close to the village was given to her "until the end of the world," and was her main residence. The hill is not a difficult climb, but be careful to shut gates as there are animals grazing over most of it. There is a palpable sense of peace here. On the hill, Áine's ancient cairn has been destroyed but there are still the remnants of three small ring-barrows known as *Mullach an Triúr*, "The Summit of the Three." These mounds have been identified with Áine's father Eogabal, her brother Fer Fí (a red-haired dwarf and musician) and Uainidhe, another mythical figure of whom little is known.

Well into the nineteenth century, a fair was held at Knockainey at the commencement of harvest, and at midsummer it was a tradition to carry the "cliara," the burning brands of hay and straw, to the top of the hill and go three times around the three mounds. The brands were then scattered in the fields and among the cattle to bring fertility for the new agricultural year. A well on the hillside is also associated with Áine, and tradition has it that it was she who built the ancient stone bridge, now lost, over the nearby river Camóg. Áine, in her later form as banshee, was often sighted combing her long hair beside the water of the Camóg and also at nearby Lough Gur. Travellers avoided spending a night on the shores of that lake, for to do so was to risk enchantment—perhaps an encounter not only with the lady of the lake herself, but also with Gearóid Iarla Fitzgerald, a historical character and a figure who, over the centuries, accrued layer after layer of folk legend. He was said to be Áine's son and a great magician who, on moonlit nights, can be seen cantering around the lake on his white horse. The lake was also believed to disappear by magic every seven years and, when that happened, the magic tree underneath the water was revealed. Under the magic tree a very old lady with long white hair was sometimes seen, knitting furiously—probably another incarnation of the local goddess. A custom which was remembered up to the 1930s was that of bringing the sick to the edge of the lake on the night when the moon was full. It was believed that even if the patients did not recover, Áine would come to them and play music to comfort them. There are also many legends associating the hero Fionn with the lake and with Áine.

The wealth of folklore in the Knockainey/Lough Gur area is not surprising, given the antiquity of the sites and the rich archaeological remains scattered through these quiet fields and hills. At Lough Gur, there is a whole complex of stone circles, pillarstones, ancient roadways and cairns. Much of the site has been excavated and is estimated to date from the Neolithic and Bronze Age periods. There is an interpretative centre and guided walks through the site. Grange Stone Circle—the largest in Ireland—is located near the shores of Lough Gur. Not far to the west is another "fairy hill," Knockfierna, home of

the god, Donn, lord of death. Fairy hares, Donn's pets, were often seen on the hill. To the north is Slieve Phelim, another legendary site; to the south, the Harps of Cliú on the Galtees; to the east, the fairy mountain of Slievenamon. There is a sense of richness in these places, both in the physical sense of green life and in the emotional sense of layer upon layer of myth and history embedded in the landscape.

In the village of Knockainey, a dog's bark is the only sound breaking the evening stillness. He stands at the gate to the ancient church and graveyard, daring the stranger to enter and disturb the sleeping dead. Cows graze in the shadow of a ruined stone castle, and the doors of the houses are open, soaking in the last of the sun. The open doors of houses give a glimpse through the darkness to white-painted panelling, a holy water font in the shape of the Virgin Mary, an oilcloth covering a table where pink ham and green lettuce have been laid out for tea. This is deep Ireland.

Above: *"Cromlech on Galtee More," by T.C. Croker.*

ÁINE OF KNOCKAINEY

The bright one, the honey mouth, the wife of the sea god and the great sky-horse, Echdae—she has appeared to so many, from the earliest times to the recent past. She is generous to those who serve her but merciless to those who do not show her respect. She is the child of the sun. She is Áine of Knockainey and Lough Gur.

Strange then, that she should appear by moonlight.

Ailill of Munster, king of the south and the man who would become known as Ailill Ólom, huddled in the lee of a rock. He wondered how he had allowed Fearcheas to convince him to come out once again on Samhain night, the most dangerous night of the year. This was the night when all sensible people kept within doors for fear of the Sídh. He sighed; he had no one to blame but himself, for he had been the one to go to the Leinster druid Fearcheas for advice. But he had been frightened by the great magic he had

Above:
Grange Stone Circle at Lough Gur, County Limerick.

seen on the Samhain morning of the previous year. That Samhain eve, he had been out on the hill, tending his horses, and had fallen into a deep sleep. When he awoke at dawn, he found that the hill had been stripped of its grass during the night and his horses were around him, hungry and dazed on the bare slopes. Ailill's motto was "What I have, I hold." Knockainey, for all they might call it a Sídh residence, was within his realm, and he wanted no host of the otherworld people denuding it of its rich grazing. So, protected by the druidic spells from sleep and from the magic mist that allowed no one to see the people of the mounds, he waited with Fearcheas to see what would happen. The moon rose, a sickle-shaped silver boat sailing gently across the sky. Shadows formed around the rocks of the hill and Ailill shivered. Despite the fact that this was the beginning of winter, there was a faint scent of hawthorn in the air. The two men waited.

When the moon had reached the pinnacle of her rising, music filled the air. It seemed to Ailill and Fearcheas that it came from inside the hill, and grew steadily louder. The scent of hawthorn grew stronger in the darkness. And then, where there had been smooth grass, there was an opening, with brightness streaming from it. A herd of cattle came forth, shining gold and silver in the moonlight, and began steadily to crop the grass of the hillside. Two people appeared out of the hill. Dazzled by the light at first, the king and the druid could not make out who the figures were; but as they came closer, they saw that it was an old man with a grave face, and a young and beautiful woman whose golden hair seemed to brighten the air around her to daylight. She was playing on the strings of a bronze *timpán*, and it was from this instrument that the wonderful music came. Ailill was suddenly filled with desire for her, and made towards her. As she turned from him, he grasped her roughly. The old man, meanwhile, began to struggle with Ailill to pull the girl away. Fearcheas threw his spear, piercing the old man through the heart. The woman cried out and dropped her *timpán*, then turned savagely to Ailill, who felt as if he had been set on fire by the warm, beautiful creature in his arms.

Minutes later, it was over. Ailill had, as ever, held what he had—he had violated the girl, and now she stood over him where he lay moaning. In her hands, she held two bloody ears.

"Well may you moan," she said. "But you who would not listen are better off without these ears to hear with. Know that you will be cursed for generations to come. You will lose your kingdom and your honour; your foul mouth will become poisonous through your own fault; and never again will you hear the sweet sound of music. Know that you will be called Ailill Ólom—Ailill of the Bald-Ears—from now on, and men will mock you and women laugh behind their hands when you pass. Know that you will know neither rest nor pleasure again."

Ailill feebly raised his spear, trying to drive it through the woman's heart, but she laughed and drew herself up to her full height so that she seemed no longer a young girl but a woman in the glory of maturity.

"Do you think that you can stop me from rising every morning? Do you not know that every day I arise, new-made, from my bed in the sea-king's kingdom? And although I seem to weaken with winter, do you not know that I rise from my cradle in the earth like the yellow corn every summer? You stupid mortal, do you still not know who I am?"

Behind her, the sky lightened and the first birds began their song. Though it was the first day of the harsh winter, though the lady was pale, and her face as cold as November ice, Ailill could be in no doubt, as the light flowed from her and encircled her head in a nimbus of glory. He was looking at the great lady Áine, goddess of the green hill and of the brightness of the sun.

Doonbeg, Clare

AN DÚN BEAG

The sandhills of Doonbeg, home of Donn, one of the great lords of the Tuatha Dé Danann, are situated in west Clare, facing the ocean. Known locally as Doughmore, the dunes are to the north of the small village of Doonbeg, and although much of the area is now enclosed by a golf club, it is still easy to reach the sandy coastal area via the small roads that run down towards the sea from the main Milltown Malbay–Kilkee Road. The village of Doonbeg is tiny, charmingly situated where the river enters the sea and surrounds the remains of a sixteenth-century castle. Though now a ruin, the castle was inhabited until 1930. The dunes themselves constitute a large area of sandhills and beach. In the late nineteenth century, there were many tales of strange lights and mysterious white horses being seen on the dunes; local people were afraid to pass through the area after dark. It was said that Donn, Lord of the Dead, had his house here, although, like so many of the Tuatha Dé Danann, he was claimed as the resident of many different districts in Ireland. In addition to Doonbeg, his home was also said to be off the coast of Béara and in Knockfierna in Limerick. The original story in *The Book of Invasions* states that Donn was one of the people of Míl, who drowned off the southwest coast as his tribe landed in Ireland. Other sources claim that he was one of the Tuatha Dé Danann, and he is closely associated with both the Cailleach Bhéarra (Hag of Béara) and Áine, goddess of the sun. He is the god who rides out to call the dead to his shadowy home. Sometimes he rides alone on his great white horse, blazing across the sky in a winter's sunset; sometimes he rides at the head of a great host, bellowing his return like the waves that beat this coast during storms; sometimes he takes the form of an animal such as a bull; and it is said that Cliodhna, one of the great banshees of Munster, changed him into a stag.

County Clare is perhaps best known for its Burren, the unique landscape of the north of the county. This bizarre area, made up of miles upon miles of karst limestone, the flat grey and white rock broken by equally stony hills, is a complete world in itself. In spring, the landscape is often the haunt of naturalists, wandering its vast surface and peering through the cracks to where bright flowers are coming up. The unique combination of shallow soil and mild wet climate has resulted in the growth of flowers native to very different environments, from the Mediterranean to the Alps. This pale world is a reflective landscape in every sense—reflective

Below:
Cratloe Castle, County Clare, by W.F. Wakeman.

almost to the extent of hypnotising the wanderer. As you walk through the Burren, the light shines back off both land and sea, and the trinity of light, stone and water has an effect which is quite literally stunning, bringing on a feeling of dislocation which is very hard to describe unless you have experienced it. The Burren is also where some of the major Megalithic remains of Clare are found, including the Polnabrone Dolmen. In contrast, the charm of the area around Doonbeg and the southern part of west Clare lies in its miles of yellow sands, its feeling of openness to wind and water and its cheerful, bucket-and-spade towns like Kilkee and Kilrush. Inland, there are green hills and fertile valleys.

However, every part of Clare shares a wealth of tales associated with ancient heroes such as Cú Chulainn, the Fianna and the Tuatha Dé Danann. Folk tradition has always been very strong in Clare and it has one of the richest musical traditions in the country. In the early twentieth century, the scholar Thomas Westropp recorded many of Clare's traditional stories, including one of the banshee, or fairy woman, which has its origins at least as far back as the eleventh century. Near Killaloe is Craglea, a great rock which is home of a great lady of the Sídh, Aoibheall. She appeared to the high king, Brian Ború, the night before the Battle of Clontarf (1014) and in the fourteenth century to the Norman knight, Richard de Clare, as he made his way to the battle of Corcomroe where his soldiers were slaughtered. On the latter occasion, she was seen washing the bloody armour of the troops at a river. Clare retained these traditions of magic into modern times—Biddy Early, the wise woman of Feakle, practised her magic until her death in 1873, and a mermaid was reportedly seen off Miltown Malbay as late as 1910.

One of the most persistent traditions of this part of the country is that of the fugitive island in the ocean to the west. The islands have been sighted from Liscannor Bay to Loop Head. Sometimes the island is the home of the dead. Sometimes it is Hy Brasil, or Manannán's Many-Coloured Land, the Land of Youth. In Liscannor Bay, the magical island is called Kilstruiteen, a place of gold and silver towers and wooded slopes which sank below the waves thousands of years ago and is seen only once every seven years. It was said that when boats passed over the place where the island was, the passengers could smell the flowers still growing under the water. This mirror-image of a lost land is one of the most powerful in Irish tradition, and, looking out towards the sun setting in the western sea, it is easy to understand why. As the day changes to night, on the deserted sands at Doonbeg, the beach becomes a liminal zone between two states of being, the tide changing the landscape even as one walks upon it. The light transforms the shapes of clouds over the water into towers and forests and valleys, and wakens some deep instinct to believe in that world, where those who are lost are talking and laughing and listening to music—the guests of an otherworld king.

DONN, LORD OF THE RED PALACE

The horns of the moon have risen over the dunes of Doonbeg, and the Lord of the Dark Face watches over the shadowy waves from his red palace, the home of those who have left life and gone to their ancestors. Kings and warriors and old wise men, smiling mothers and proud queens, mourning widows and merry girls—all of them come home to Donn's house, far to the southwest of Ireland.

The waves are still tonight, and Donn has not yet made his journey to summon those whom he will take to his home. He is the lord of shadow, of storms and shipwrecks and those who die with blood upon them. Unlike the Morrigan, however, he does not glory in slaughter. He is the god of truth as well as death, for death is the inescapable last truth. His sister is the goddess Áine of Knockainey, the goddess with the face of the sun. He knows that even the people of the Sídh, bright and powerful as they are, will finally come to his shadowy house. He watches and waits quietly in the darkness.

And tonight, someone has come to beg a boon of him.

Fionn is known by all as a great hunter, a great warrior, a great womaniser, a great giver of gifts and hospitality, and an even greater boaster about his own past. He is fair-haired and broad-shouldered and, when the two men stand together, it would seem that he should be the one granting the favours. But that is not the case—Fionn has come to plead for a gift for one of his companions. For, in addition to his other attributes, Fionn has great loyalty to his friends. He has made the journey to the House of Donn out of concern for one beloved to him.

"Lord Donn," Fionn says, bowing very low. "My musician, Cnú Dearóil, is a sad and lonely man, for he has no wife. Usually, this would not be a problem, for I could easily find one for him from the numerous princesses, fairy-women, messengers and seers that gather around me and the Fianna, like bees around honey. But there is a problem, my lord. Cnú Dearóil is no taller than four of my fists, though he is the greatest musician the world has ever known. Gracious Lord Donn, if you were to hear him play, even you would be impressed. Warriors suffering from the wounds of battle and women in labour fall asleep when Cnú Dearóil plays his lullabies. So I have

come to you, great lord of the otherworld, to beg for a wife of a suitable size for my friend."

Lord Donn considers for a moment, and then nods his head graciously. "I will see what can be done," he promises.

And he is as good as his word, for within his realm he finds the musician a wife as fair as a May blossom. She is called Bláthnuit, meaning "Little Blossom", and she is no bigger than Cnú Dearóil himself. The pair live together for many happy years, travelling on Fionn's horse on his journeys throughout Ireland, taking refuge from the rain under his cloak. When they die, they too are welcomed into the House of Donn, and Cnú Dearóil plays the music that lets the dead forget their past sorrows.

In his dealings with the great ones, with warriors like Fionn and kings and princesses, Donn was often generous. But Donn was not generous only to the rich and mighty. He has been seen wearing a black silk hat, giving alms to a widow who went outside her house so that her starving children should not see her weep on a hungry Christmas Eve. He saved the cattle of a local herdsman from theft. His horses are often heard at *Cnoc an Sodair*, the Hill of the Trotting, near the shore at the dunes, and his lights are seen over the same dunes where those he has brought home feast with him, listening to the music made in his dark tower. He gives the best to his guests—the willowy girls and blue-eyed athletes, the grey-haired widows and toothless, tired old men. For the Lord of Death is courteous, and not just in giving the gifts of life. Sometimes, and not rarely, when he calls those who have lived too long or have suffered too much, he is more than courteous—he is kind.

Opposite:
The ruins of Doonbeg Castle, County Clare.

Connacht

Dún Aonghusa, the Aran Islands, Galway

ÁRAINN MHÓR

If certain places have their defining myths—the story that seems best to embody the experience of the place and of the people who have lived there—the myth of the Aran Islands must be one of survival. Survival against the harshness of the elements, the wild western sea and ferocious winds coming in over the Atlantic; survival in a hard and inhospitable landscape. The islands are made up of the same grey carboniferous limestone pavement that covers the Burren, and what little soil there is is the result of back-breaking effort on the part of the human population. The tiny, stone-walled fields were created from sand and seaweed and broken shells. Because there are few trees—what there are are low-lying hawthorn and hazel—and no turf, at one time even fuel was at a premium, ferried in from Galway on the famous hookers. It was not an easy existence, but the community survived.

And what also survived were ancient customs, an ancient language and one of the most impressive monuments of ancient Ireland—the great fort of Dún Aonghusa.

The fort is situated on the largest of the Aran Islands, Inishmore. It dominates the island. Its situation is one of astounding natural drama and beauty. Built on the edge of cliffs almost 100 metres (328 feet) above sea level, the stone fort is made up of three widely spaced horseshoe-shaped walls. The walls are massive and the complex covers 4.5 hectares (11 acres) of land. One of the most impressive features is the middle rampart of *chevaux de frise*, where jagged limestone rocks form an impenetrable barrier to the inner area. There is a single entrance through this army of stones to the open spaces of the innermost court and the natural stone platform near the edge of the precipice.

In mythological terms, Dún Aonghusa does not seem to have any connection with the god of the Tuatha Dé Danann, Aonghus Óg. The fort was said to have been built by another Aengus, the last king of the Fir Bolg. The Fir Bolg were one of the ancient tribes of Ireland who were gradually driven to the extreme western shores of the country before their final defeat. There has been ongoing controversy over the function and dating of Dún Aonghusa. The huge effort put into the defences may suggest a refuge, although some archaeologists have dismissed this

Pages 128-129:
Abbey of Cong, County Mayo.
Above:
An engraving of the stone fort of Dún Aonghusa, the Aran Islands, Galway.

theory, because of the lack of water on the site. Excavations show evidence of settlement on the site dating back to the Bronze Age, although other parts of the structure seem to have been built in the Iron Age, and there is evidence of burial here as late as the tenth century. The fort seems to have been most in use, almost certainly as a centre for ceremonial gatherings—the traditional *aonach*—between 800BC and 400AD.

The restoration work carried out at the end of the nineteenth century was faithful to the original layout and Dún Aonghusa is one of the most dramatic of all the Irish forts. The people who built this structure were undoubtedly intent on showing their power and overawing the visitor—and they succeeded. The visitor cannot but look with awe at the mighty *dún*, even now, during the summer months, when it is difficult to find a day when the site is not swarming with tourists. Inishmore's current visitor numbers are in excess of 200,000 every year. Instead of the traditional Aran bright red petticoats, it is brightly coloured windcheaters—at times it feels like thousands of them—that make the short trip from the ferry to Dún Aonghusa, their numbers standing out even more clearly because of the wide, open, grey-stone landscape. As a result of easier access and successful marketing, the old days, when the hardship of life on Aran was written about and sometimes romanticised by the many writers who were inspired by the islands, have gone forever. Inishmore, as the largest and most easily accessible of the three islands, has perhaps suffered the most change.

Is it hypocritical for someone who visited these islands as a tourist to lament the loss of the old Aran? The antiquaries, the botanists, the writers and the painters have, through their celebration of the island, brought about its transformation. Yet perhaps there is no need to be overly pessimistic. During the summer months, wild roses still cover the grey rocks and the small roads of the island, as well as the ancient remains of mysterious structures such as the Black Fort and Dún Eoghanachta. The many other archaeological sites on the island also include a wealth of early Christian antiquities. And unlike many western islands, a thriving community survives here.

It is said that at one stage Inishmore, which is closely associated with St. Enda, who sailed to the island on a stone and founded a monastery here, was a pilgrimage site on par with Rome and Jerusalem. The islands were known as "Aran of the Saints." Perhaps "Aran of the Tourists" may be a more appropriate title now, but if the people of Aran adapt their survival skills to the problems which confront them in their success, the pilgrims of the twenty-first century will continue to find meaning in this place of bleak beauty and enduring monuments. Stone, after all, is one of the great survivors.

THE LAST OF THE FIR BOLG

Over the ocean, the red sun was setting; a faint mist rose from the sea. A world of stone surrounded Aengus, the Son of Umor, as he sat on the ramparts of the Dún Aonghusa, the mighty fort that bore his name. His sword arm was wounded, and blood—some old, some fresh—seeped through the bandage. It was winter, and too cold to be sitting out there, but the king had no heart to go inside, where bodies lay piled and the sick lay moaning. There was no one left with the strength to help them.

It was the end of the Fir Bolg, the great race that had built the ramparts on the west of the island of Inishmore, in high, inhospitable places, facing the ocean over which they had come so many centuries before. Here his people had come to offer him tribute, to make treaties between the tribes, to worship their gods and race horses and contest their skills. His people had once ruled all of Ireland. Aengus remembered the stories of his youth, when the singers of his people had filled his imagination with the great tales of his ancestors. The people of Bolg, the god of lightning and flame, were descended from Nemed, one of the first men to come to the land of Ireland. The Nemedians had defeated the Fomorians, the black and crooked sea-pirates who had held the land in subjection. However, when the Nemedians had attacked the tower of Fomorians, a great wave had come and drowned all but a handful of the attackers. Those who were left had scattered then; some had gone to Britain and some to the northern places where they learned the ways of magic. The Fir Bolg had gone to Greece, but had not forgotten, in their stories and songs, the green, fertile land to the west.

After two centuries, they had returned, dividing Ireland into five provinces, each one ruled by one of their leaders. They had governed the country for many years, but then the Tuatha Dé Danann had come. The Tuatha Dé Danann were also the descendants of Nemed, but in this case of those Nemedians who had gone to the northern islands and had come back with magical powers, landing in a haze of mist and smoke and bringing new and powerful gods with them. They had defeated the Fir Bolg and the Fomorians who had fought side by side at the Battle of Moytura (*Magh Tuiredh*), the Plain of Pillars, forgetting their old enmity in their need to defeat the new invaders. The Fir Bolg had fled to the islands of Scotland; and there, the sons of Umor had been born. But still the dream of ruling Ireland remained and, after twenty-seven years, Aengus had led his people back to Ireland.

Above:
The great stone fort of Dún Aonghusa, the Aran Islands, Galway.

It was a changed Ireland, for the conquering Dé Danann had themselves been defeated by the Sons of Míl, and a new king reigned at Tara. King Cairbre had at first welcomed the Fir Bolg, but as time went on, he had become more and more wary of their power and had imposed heavy taxes on them. Finally, the Fir Bolg had fled west and set up their kingdom on Galway Bay. Their realm had stretched from Black Head to Ballyvaughan, and they had built great forts along the line of their jurisdiction.

However, Cairbre had been watching from the east, fearful of their power, and had finally sent warriors against them. Bloody battles had been fought, with great losses on both sides, until Aengus had sent his three brothers and his son, Conall, to fight the four mighty warriors who led the enemy: Ceat Mac Maghach, Conall Cearnach, Ros Mac Deadha and the great Cú Chulainn himself. Aengus's beloved son, Conall, had fought against the Hound of Ulster, and had been killed by a blow from the *Gáe Bolg*, the fiery bolt which was Cú Chulainn's invincible weapon.

Conall had been young, and had held the promise of being a great king.

Why hold on to my kingdom, thought Aengus, if there is no child to hand it on to? Why try to lead on a people who are dying all around me? Why try to hold my name when there is no one to pass it on to?

He looked to the sky, waiting to hear the voice of the Lord of Storms, waiting to see the sky split open and the heavens descend in a deluge of water and wind. But there was only the sea; blood red as the sun sank into it. And the white stone all around him—hard, ungiving and silent.

There was water in his eyes—whether from the spray of the ocean or something else Aengus was not prepared to question—and a smell of salt and blood on the wind. The king looked down to the pale rocks under his feet, to where the delicate white bones of a seagull lay crushed, and beside them the remains of the broken egg of some bird. Then he arose and went to buckle on sword and shield and take up his spear, for all that was left for him to do was to die fighting the enemies of his people. In a time as short as the wink of a god's eye, nothing would be left of him or his race but a fortress of stone on the edge of the world, carrying his name and the bloodline of a dark race.

Lough Corrib, Galway

LOCH COIRIB

Lough Corrib, the lake sacred to the god Manannán, is situated north of Galway city and touches Mayo on its northern flank. It is the second largest lake in Ireland and is bordered by a variety of landscapes. Approximately 56 kilometres (35 miles) long, it varies greatly in width and is dotted by no fewer than 145 islands. It is said that Manannán, taking on the shape of a mortal called Oirbsiu, was killed by Uillen Red Edge at the battle of Cuillen. Loch Corrib rose where his blood spilled, bringing his mortal flesh back into the watery, immortal world that is his realm. If that is the case, and god is dead, the lake is a worthy tomb. Rushes, sacred to this particular god, grow around it and it changes shape and character as often as a cloud blows across the sun and shadows cross this world of water and mist and wooded islets. Manannán himself was a trickster, changing shape as often

as water—sometimes an old man in a grey cloak, sometimes a great warrior riding the waves like horses. He was called Manawyddan in Wales and was also the three-legged solar god from which the Isle of Man takes its name. His wives were Áine, the sun-goddess of the south (though some say that she is his daughter) and Fand, the woman of the Sídh who loved Cú Chulainn so desperately. He shook his cloak between Fand and Cú Chulainn so that the memory of their mad love should fade from their hearts. He had many children, and his daughter lakes are Sheelin and Ennell, Owel and Derravaragh. One of his sons was the great king Mongan, the shape-changer; one of his foster-sons was Lugh, the many-skilled god.

Above:
Lough Corrib.

He gave the Sídh the gift of invisibility and shape-changing, and some say that it was he who divided the palaces in the hollow hills among the Tuatha Dé Danann after their defeat by the Milesians. It was he who instigated the feast of Goibhniu, where food never runs out, and the people of Danu are renewed and made young again. The pigs of Manannán, when killed and eaten, rise up the next day, ready again for the feast.

The eastern side of Manannán's lake is flat and less beautiful than the west, although there are still interesting sites to visit. One of these is Annaghdown, a village with a substantial complex of ecclesiastical remains, and the site of the drowning of Annach Cuan. The story of this tragic drowning gave rise to one of the loveliest songs in the Irish language, "Annach Cuan." Knockma, the home of the fairy king, Finvarra, is also near this part of the lake.

In contrast to the east side of the lake, its north and western perimeters border Connemara, which has some of the wildest and most dramatic scenery in Ireland. It is this mixture of landscape—pasture and woodland, rock and bog, islands and lake—which give the lake its unique character. One of the most beautiful parts of the lakeshore is around the villages of Cong and Clonbur on its northern tip. The towering mountains are relieved by the presence of the lovely wooded slopes of the river which flows through Cong. Cong itself is a tiny village and, although it is heavily frequented by tourists, it is still, with a fine Augustinian priory, a beautiful place to visit. The monastic settlement here originally dated from the seventh century. The underlying rock in this area is limestone, and is fissured with caverns and underground rivers—a world of constant subterranean activity. To the north of the village is the Plain of Moytura—the place claimed by William Wilde, the famous Oscar's father, as the site of the first battle of the Dé Danaans against their enemies the Fir Bolg. Most authorities now assert that both battles took place at the site near Lough Arrow in Sligo, but Wilde's theory was supported by the very large number of prehistoric antiquities—particularly cairns—in the surrounding district. Early Christian remains are also plentiful; some of the most atmospheric are on the island of Inchagoill, which can be reached by ferry from Cong. This wooded graveyard was in use until relatively recently, and there are substantial Romanesque ecclesiastical remains. There is also the Stone of Lugha, which is one of the earliest Christian inscriptions in Ireland.

Below:
Ruins of Cong Abbey, County Mayo.

Travelling on the lake is probably one of the easiest ways to get a sense of this watery, woody landscape. Another, slightly more difficult one is to hike up into the mountains around Clonbur and Cornamona. Here one enters a world of shifting mists and unexpected sunlight, of rain that covers the patchwork of bright fields in a watery haze and then, just as suddenly, passes over. Our minds stained by our technicoloured culture, we find the effects almost too much. How can these colours, this light, be real? Is Maureen O'Hara about to come tripping over that emerald-green hilltop? Where is the Hollywood cameraman hiding—the master of illusion who just this second decided to light up that particular island with yet another rainbow? Or was that improbable band of colour beaming in a message from that other great trickster—was that really a sign from Manannán's Many-Coloured Land?

MANANNÁN AND THE CRANE BAG

Above:
A view over Lough Corrib.

A fine, mackerel-skied evening over the silver sea, and the Son of Lir was out riding his great horse, Waterfoam, skimming over the waves, surveying his realm. To him, the ocean is a purple-flecked pasture of flowers, the salmon its lambs, leaping high in the water. He is equally at home over and under the waves, bringing some chosen ones, like Connla and Bran and the great King Cormac, to visit him in the Apple Isle, the Land of Promise. In his kingdom, blue and crimson horses graze, gold and silver birds sing in trees with shining leaves, and there are houses of white bronze, set with jewels and crystals and thatched with white feathers. This day he had been out hunting, with his spear and his bow in his hands, scanning the skies for birds to bring home to the feast. Now it was evening, with a golden sky to the west, and he had turned in towards the mountains, hoping that there he might capture an eagle or a sparrowhawk.

He narrowed his eyes against the setting sun—surely there was a bird, an exceptionally large and beautiful one, flying high over the lakes in the valleys between the high hills of Connemara. It was a crane, by the look of its red crown on the black plumage of its head, he decided as he fitted an arrow into his bow and took aim. He had no time for the thought to form in his head that there was something strange, not quite normal, about the path of the bird's flight or its high, lonely call. The arrow had already sped from the bow and was shimmering in the evening sunlight, its path straight and true to the bird's heart. Then there was a cry, and the feathery mass plummeted through the air and sank to the ground on the far side of the lough. Manannán raced his horse across the water to where it had fallen, and was in time to see the change shimmering through: the fair-skinned face through the brownish-grey feathers, the slender limbs through the bird's trailing legs and webbed feet. And the dying creature spoke to him in a human voice: "Whoever you are, man or god, you must know that you have killed Aife, daughter of Dealbheath, himself the son of honey-tongued Ogma. I was the most beloved of princesses, and I wished no harm to anyone, until the enchantress Luchra turned me into this form, for she loved the man who loved only me. Since then I have flown over these hills and islands, seeking to keep track of my beloved. He is a poet, and he has wandered all over Ireland searching for me, for he thinks that I have forsaken him. The poems he writes about me and the love that he has for me break my heart, and yet they are the only consolation I have known since I took this body. But now I think that I must be leaving this body too, for see how the blood flows ..."

Aife's voice faded, and the bird form again took over—a lovely creature with soft plumage and the light dying in its eyes. The god looked on helplessly, for even his powers could not restore life to her. Then he said to the dying bird-woman: "I will take your body, the body of this winged creature, at home in the water and in the air, and from its skin I will make a bag. This bag will be a thing of great power and enchantment, for when the tide is in and the sea is full, the treasures of the crane bag will be seen, but when it is in ebb, it will seem empty."

Aife died then, and the god Manannán kept his word. From that day, cranes became sacred birds, never to be killed or eaten. The bag he made from the skin of Aife holds the secret things of the Tuatha Dé Danann: the bones of the sacred boar, the smith's hook and the magical knife, shield and shirt. Whoever has these weapons is safe from all enemies. And Manannán gave the bag one further power, perhaps greater than all of these. The crane bag holds the source of inspiration for all the poets of the land. In this way, Aife's loving heart was made immortal.

Inis Glora *and the* Erris Peninsula, Mayo

INIS GLÓIRE

The story of the Children of Lir is most commonly associated with beautiful Lake Derravaragh in County Westmeath. In many ways, however, the legend of Lir's children is a story of loneliness, and it is therefore closely bound in spirit to the place where their story ends. Inis Glora is a tiny island on the west coast of the Mullet peninsula in northwest Mayo. West Mayo is a place of spectacular beauty and spectacular loneliness, and of all its solitary places, the Mullet peninsula is one of the most isolated. The peninsula consists of a long isthmus joined to the mainland by only a thin neck of land. The nearest towns are Castlebar, Westport and Ballina. These towns buzz with people, but none of them is nearer than 50 kilometres (31 miles) away.

The journey from these towns to Belmullet seems even longer than the mileage would indicate because the road takes the traveller through an unrelenting landscape of high mountains, rocky passes, and most of all, blanket bog. This stunning but desolate landscape is barely relieved by a house, much less a village. Boglands have a particular atmosphere which is all their own. No crops can be grown there; no animals can graze there. They contain great riches of plant life but the overriding feeling of travelling through such a landscape is one of desolation. It has a strange, slightly uncomfortable beauty. The bogs are the Irish equivalent of the desert—a desert made up of brown earth and water and open skies; a place in which the individual feels very small against the vastness of a landscape that seems untouched by humanity. The boglands are also preservers—indeed petrifiers of the past, a growing and living memory of the race. When the tracts of bogs at the Céide Fields in Mayo were excavated, extensive remains of a highly organised prehistoric landscape of fields and structures was discovered under the blanket of turf. The dark tower of Bellacorrick power station stands out in harsh contrast to its surrounding bog, the source of its fuel. One wonders if in future years our descendants will look back on the stripping of the bog in the same way that we look back in sadness at the clearing of the great Irish forests.

Perhaps the feeling of loneliness in Mayo is increased by the knowledge that this is not a countryside that was never settled, but one that once had a much higher population than it has now. Mayo was one of the counties that suffered most from the disasters of the nineteenth century,

Below: *View of Clew Bay and Croagh Patrick, County Mayo, by F.W. Fairholt.*

particularly the Great Famine and the ensuing mass emigration. Up until very recently, a huge percentage of its young people were still being leached from its soil. Now, however, the empty landscape is beginning to be filled with new houses—during the past five years, Belmullet has seen growth and prosperity probably unknown since its hey-day as a market town in the mid-nineteenth century. Yet, despite its new wealth, the smells of turf smoke and seaweed still linger in its small harbour.

Inis Glora, however, has lost its human community, possibly forever. Like the neighbouring Iniskea islands, it was inhabited until the mid-1930s, but the island community was shattered in 1927 when ten of its people were drowned at sea. Up until more recently, fishermen lived on the islands during the summer and worked the seas off their coasts, but this too has ceased. There is no regular boat service to Inis Glora, and if you wish to visit it, you must make your arrangements well in advance—it was only the native courtesy and sense of hospitality of the Mayo people which got us there at all.

If you can manage it, make the journey. The island is about 3 kilometres (less than 2 miles) offshore and is only about 27 hectares (66 acres) in size. There is no pier so you would need to be reasonably agile—and wearing wellingtons—for the scramble onto the rocky shore. On the island, there are the remains of a Celtic monastic settlement said to have been founded by St. Brendan. You will also find the remnants of a stone church and some beehive huts, together with various other enclosures, including the church of the women. It was said that bodies buried in the soil here did not rot, because the place was so sacred.

The island is deserted now except for sea birds and some sheep. There are no beaches, but lovely golden and pink stones veined with silver line the shore and long ridges from old potato crops, like giants' graves, cover much of the interior—a record of the lost community. During our visit there, a gull circled noisily overhead, as if warning us off her property. She became particularly vociferous as we walked to the southern end of the island, away from the Christian section. Here there are mounds of broken stone, littered with the bones and feathers of birds, with sheep skulls and brown pools between the rocks. The patterns of the bright tawny lichen on the stones are uncannily like the spirals and semi-spirals, the circles and cup marks of the Megalithic art found at Knowth.

Even if you do not make it to the island, the peninsula itself is a beautiful place to visit. It is covered in extensive early Christian and Megalithic remains. It was the reputed home of Fliodhas, the wife of Fergus Mac Róich and an ancient goddess of wild things, especially deer. The Mullet is a place of long, deserted beaches—pale dunes filled with small singing birds and long grass bending in the wind. In summer, the shades of blue on the distant mountains darken into black and purple; and the lighter greys and silvers also constantly shift and change. These are some of the most beautiful views in Ireland, towards the deceptively gentle line of mountains to the south, with the cliffs and mountains of Achill and the southern coastline of Mayo. Achill is where the great Hawk of Achill, who lived for thousands of years, was said to have had his home. To the south, beyond Achill, is the holy mountain, Croagh Patrick, one of the most revered places in Ireland, where a pilgrimage is still held in July every year—a continuation of the ancient Lughnasa rite. St. Patrick is said to have been tormented by black-winged birds on "the Reek," and then comforted by angels with white wings, who came to him in multitudes—one angel for every soul saved in Ireland.

In the townland of Cross on the Mullet, Cross Abbey stands on the coast facing towards Inis Glora at the closest point to the island. Beside a long white beach there are still the remains of a monastery and graveyard. The monks from Inis Glora moved here after they had left the island. Close by, you can visit Cross Lake, which is said to have been a refuge of the Children of Lir during wild winter weather. If you make the journey to the lake in winter, when it becomes the haunt of barnacle geese and whooper swans, you may see white wings flying out towards the lonely island in the west.

THE CHILDREN OF LIR

The moment of transformation—from fair day to storm, from maiden to wife, from good woman to demon, from white-limbed child to swan. Four pairs of grey eyes staring at me in horror as I transformed myself before their very eyes from loving mother into wicked witch. The eyes that looked at me were my sisters' eyes, and my own eyes, for everyone said that we were as alike as three peas in a pod, the fair daughters of Bodhbh—Aobh, Aoife and Ailbhe. Why did Lir not choose me in the first place? My father offered him the choice; but he chose my elder sister, seeing in her wisdom and nobility.

He did not hear me calling silently to him, "Choose me, Prince. Choose me."

My sister Aobh did not have time to grow old and wise, for she died when she bore her second set of twins, Conn and Fiachra. The eldest pair, Fionnuala and Aodh, were still not much more than babies. And then my father called Lir to him again and offered me to him—Aoife, the second sister, the second best—and he agreed to take me then, but his face and his heart were closed against me.

I loved my husband and I loved my sister's children, and for many years, I was a good wife and a good mother, while I waited to have my own child—a child to whom I would be the first, the most important one, the real mother. When that did not happen, it seemed that nobody cared very much. Lir had his four children—three sons and a fine daughter—and my father his grandchildren. As they grew up, it seemed that Fionnuala was set to rival my sister in the love she inspired in all who had dealings with her. It is hard to be always second choice. The children made their own self-contained little world: two sets of twins, indissolubly linked, unheeding of my pleas to let me into their tightly closed circle. And that was perhaps why I became bitter and sick, and I lay in my bed for a year and waited for someone to notice. Something grew and hardened in me during that year. Lir would come and ask me how I felt, but did not listen for my answer. Fionnuala would come with the boys, shushing them to be quiet so as not to disturb me. I could hear their relieved laughter when they left me. Life went on around me.

One autumn morning, I got up and called the children to me. I told them that they were going to visit their grandfather, and they were delighted—all but Fionnuala, who looked at me strangely and when I asked her what was the matter, said that she had not slept well, a night of bad dreams.

I took them in my chariot to Lake Derravaragh, and told them to bathe, for although it was the end of the year, the air was mild and the water warm. As I watched them in the water, their white limbs dancing in the low sunlight, splashing and playing and singing and laughing, I knew that I could not kill them. So I took my wand and pronounced their doom, and looked on as the white feathers sprouted on their flesh, their necks growing longer, their feet becoming webbed and their legs short and unwieldy.

"You shall spend the rest of your days as swans," I said. "Three hundred years you will spend here at this lake, then three hundred years on the Sea of Moyle. Do you know the Sea of Moyle? It is one of the wildest and coldest

Above: *The ruins of Cross Abbey standing on the coast, facing towards Inis Glora, County Mayo.*

seas in the world. Your webbed feet will freeze to the rocks, so that when you try to get loose, you will tear your feet, and when you swim, the salt water will be agony.

"The last three hundred years you will spend on Inis Glora, in the western ocean. You shall not be released from this spell until the man of the north marries the woman from the south. But I will give you one boon—during all this time, you will retain your human minds and your human voices, and you will sing such music that all who hear you will be astounded, and however sad they are, they will be comforted."

And then I could look at them no more, but made my way to my father's palace. His face dropped when he saw that I was alone, and the bitterness in my heart increased. Of course, it was not long before the people of Danu discovered my evil-doing; and my own father in his great anger turned me into a demon of the air, condemned to fly and wander in exile forever, terrifying all who saw or heard me.

The moment of transformation—from good daughter to shrieking demon, from one of the tribe to the one who will always be an exile. Fionnuala, Aodh, Conn and Fiachra had an easier time of it than I did, for during their three hundred years on the lake, the Danann came and listened to them and cheered them; and their music comforted all who heard it—all, that is, except me. But then they went to the Sea of Moyle, and that was a hard time for them, for the storms beat their soft feathers, and the ice froze their feet to the sharp rocks, and the wind drowned out their singing; and no one was within miles to listen to their music in any case, except poor sailors blown off course who covered their ears for fear of the treacherous songs of mermaids. Fionnuala would try to shelter her brothers under her wings and at the pin-feathers of her breast, and it was only the heat of the four bodies that kept them alive on many, many nights. Often, though, they would be blown apart, separated from each other, and each one found those wild, lonely nights the hardest—not knowing if they would meet again.

How do I know this? I know because I was there, hating them still, but still their mother, watching over them—needing to know that they still suffered. Those wild nights were the only ones where I myself escaped my pain. For, buffeted by wild wind and crashing waves, I was released from the anger that burnt inside me. The wildness of the storms carried me to some other place where I no longer needed love, and my rage was called back to me in the wind and the water.

However, that too finally ended, and the four swans made their way westwards, passing over their father's *sídh* at Sídh Fionnachaidh. They called aloud as they passed over, and the Danann looked up at the four magical birds, so white against the blue sky of autumn; they waved at them but the four children did not stop, for the times had changed. The Sídh now disguised their palaces as grassy mounds, hiding them from the eyes of the new race that lived in Ireland. The Place of the White Field seemed to the swans no more than green mounds and furze and crops of nettles—not jewelled palaces and lovely orchards; not houses thatched with white feathers. The song they sang then was so mournful that I think if I had had any heart left, it would have been broken by the music. Meanwhile, below, the Danann called to them in frantic voices to come home, come back to their loved ones. They flew on, unable to hear, far to the west and to the shores of the great ocean.

And there, on Inis Glora, they found a lake on an island, where they made their last home. Their music was such that it drew birds from everywhere around. And after another three hundred years had come and gone, I heard new sounds on the island—the chant of Latin and the tolling of a bell. A hermit came there—a gentle man who listened to the birds every evening, and they told him their tale. He made silver chains for them, which held them together, so that no matter how wild the storms were, they could never become separated. I hid in the trees by the lake, silent and watchful, knowing that the day would finally come when the enchantment would end.

A princess from the south married a prince from the north, and, having heard of the wonderful music of the four swans that lived on Inis Glora, she demanded them as a bridal gift from her husband. But when the prince came to fetch them, the hermit Mochaomhóg refused to give them up. The prince became angry and made to take them by force from where they stood by the altar in the hermit's tiny church.

And then again, the moment of transformation—from swan to human. Not to godlike children, on the verge of blossoming, but to four withered old people, bent and broken, ready for death—children who had never grown up, had never known the pain of not being loved enough; children who had found love even in the shape of wild swans; children who were nearly a thousand years old.

Then Fionnuala said, in a cracked voice that was hardly above a whisper, "Brother Mochaomhóg, our time is not long. Baptise us now, and bury us together in the churchyard of your god. Bury Conn on my right and Fiachra on my left, and place Aodh before me, for it was so we used to stand on the rocks of the Sea of Moyle when the wind buffeted us, during so many cold and bitter nights."

So the children of the Sídh were transformed into good Christian corpses and buried far from the mounds of their people. The hermit mourned them greatly. He still goes to the lake in the evening, but it is silent now except for the harsh call of the gulls; all the birds that sang there once have fled. My voice has called to him once or twice, but he does not even hear me above his prayers. I continue to live, without the mercy of death. I suffer more than the children ever suffered. They have found release in their last transformation—to bleached bones buried beside a priest's cell. I am what I have always been. With no hope of rest or change, I make my cries, shrieking my pain over barren islands, limitless oceans, salt foam white as a swan's wing.

Rathcroghan, Roscommon

CRUACHAIN

The road between the small Roscommon village of Tulsk and the town of Ballaghadereen travels through the site of one of the most important ancient ritual centres on the whole island of Ireland. It is easy to pass by without realising this. Perhaps the sight of a green mound on the side of the road might stir a memory of ancient Cruachain, home of the warrior queen, Maeve; or perhaps, passing through Tulsk, you might stop for a coffee at the Heritage Centre and discover that there is a world of ancient magical places surrounding the village. Even among those interested in mythology and archaeology, Rathcroghan is surprisingly little known and explored. The site covers 6 kilometres (almost 4 miles) and includes over 80 different pre-Norman features. There are monuments dating from various periods—Megalithic tombs, Bronze Age cairns and forts of the early Christian period. Within the complex, there are acres of unexplored mounds and a cave reputed to be the entry to the otherworld.

Above:
Tulsk Abbey, County Roscommon.

Detailed surveying of this huge site began only in the 1980s, and excavation of the features is still in the early stages. Many of the structures remain a mystery but some certainly date back to 3000BC. *Ráth Cruachain*, or Cruachain Fort, the largest mound in the complex, is easily accessible from the road, and this is traditionally held to be the place where the quarrel between Ailill and Maeve began over who had the greatest wealth. This was the quarrel which started the Táin, Ireland's great epic. As with so many of these sites, Iron Age dwellings were built on the site of much older structures, often graves, because these places had been held sacred over many centuries. Ráth Cruachain is not a high mound, but like Tara, it gives the sense of altitude and distance—of imperial powers looking over acres of land and claiming it as a kingdom. The sky is wide and the surrounding land flat, but not boggy—this is good, fertile grazing land.

To the south of the mound, there are traces of an ancient avenue, running east to west, which was probably used in the ceremonies held here at Samhain, the cusp of the new year, when Maeve would consult with her druids as to what the future year might bring to her and her people. During my visit on a bright winter's day, the outlines of the hills seemed etched in some hard, bright metal—silver or perhaps iron—and the land itself, with its smooth green mounds, leaves a sense of a landscape little changed over long centuries. It is easy to imagine the herds of cattle and flocks of sheep, the horses and pigs and dairy cows, being herded before Maeve and Ailill, and the people moving backwards and forwards from their wattle

huts, sheltered by earthen mounds and wooden fences. As the red sun sets in the sky, it is also easy to imagine the warriors gathering, filling the plains as far as the eye can see, readying themselves for their march to Ulster and to death.

Rathnadarve or *Ráth na dTarbh*, the Fort of the Bulls, is a large ring-barrow, situated near Ráth Cruachain at Ballymacthomas. According to local tradition, this is the circular earthen stockade where the Brown Bull and the White Bull were herded together to fight their last battle. Nearby is Oweynagat or *Uaimh na gCat*, the Cave of the Cats, a place steeped in local folklore and myth. Access to the cave is possible, though wet-weather gear is essential. In 1779, it was still known as the Hell-Mouth of Ireland, a tradition that had survived for thousands of years. In this cave, the war-goddess, the Morrigan, was said to live, and, at Samhain, magic pigs and bronze-beaked birds issued forth from it. The great hero, Nera, entered the underworld through Owneygat. A further legend links the cave with a tunnel connecting it with the caves of Keshcorann in Sligo, another home of malevolent female deities. Mirroring this site of otherworld power, at Carnfree, south of Tulsk, there is a centre of earthly power which, in historical times, was the inauguration site of the O'Conors, kings of Connacht.

Cruachain continued as an important centre of assembly well into the beginning of the Christian era; it may have been deserted as late as the beginning of the ninth century. Legend has it that Christianity came here with St. Patrick, who met the two daughters of the King of Leinster as they were learning the ways of magic from the Cruachain druids, at Ogulla or Clebach well, southwest of Tulsk. As was usual with these stories, the two maidens enthusiastically embraced the Christian faith and died directly after having received baptism. The well is still the site of a local pattern and is well cared for by the people of the village. In fact, Rathcroghan has been fortunate in that the population has respected the monuments enough to keep them preserved through many centuries. The local community has now established

Above:
Pagan and Christian cultures meet at Cruachain.

an excellent interpretative centre which helps greatly in putting the locality into context. However, nothing can really compete with visiting the mounds themselves and watching the flocks of birds blown across the plains by a wind as fierce and relentless as the will of Connacht's ancient queen.

PILLOW TALK:
The Beginning of the Táin Bó Cuailgne

The marital bed at Rathcroghan was vast and deep, and Ailill Mac Máta never questioned who his wife and consort, Queen Maeve of Connacht, brought into it. She had married him not only because he was a king in his own right, but because he was a man who would not be mean, or cowardly, or jealous; she boasted that she never had one man without another waiting in his shadow. Ailill had reason to know the truth of this, for at the moment he was quite sure that his wife was sleeping with Fergus Mac Róich, the Ulster warrior who had taken refuge in the court of Cruachain after Conchobhar Mac Neasa had tricked him into betraying the Sons of Usna. Fergus was an embittered man, but nonetheless a great warrior and a clever counsellor; still, Ailill wondered if his wife really had to give him the friendship of her thighs as well as that of her court in order to keep him in their camp.

He looked down at her while she slept, her straight yellow hair loose on the fine pillows, her grey eyes closed; for once, her long face was peaceful, but Ailill knew that just as soon as she woke there would be plots and dissension and sometimes, and not rarely, false promises coming from that lovely mouth. However, times had been quiet lately and the land rich in herds, the rivals to their power lying low before the combined strength of Maeve and Ailill. They knew the ruthlessness of Maeve—she had killed her sister in order to rule at Rathcroghan and she would kill, sell or barter any of her loved ones to keep it and to keep her power. Ailill's face was tender as he looked at her, for she held her husband's devotion like she held her great wolfhounds, tight to her side on a short leash, easily brought to heel. Yet, deep down, he thought to himself that she was lucky to have him, for there were not many who could have put up with her scheming and her temper.

As he watched the sunlight streaming down on his wife's face, she opened one eye and looked at him. Maeve, when she awoke, awoke like a warrior, fully alert and ready for battle.

"What is it?" she asked, "What are you thinking of?"

"Ah, nothing really," said Ailill.

"Go on, then," said Maeve. "You must have been thinking of something."

Ailill answered at random: "I was just thinking that you were a lucky woman to have married me."

Maeve sat up against the pillows and narrowed her eyes.

"And what do you mean by that?"

Ailill shrugged. He was beginning to regret that he had started this conversation.

"Only that you are better off now than the day you married me."

"Am I indeed? And are you not better off that I took you still young and brought you to my bed and gave such gifts to you? I was the highest and mightiest, the bravest in battle of my father's six daughters, and that is why I rule in his place. Look at the soldiers I have and the common men and the herds and the bondmaids and the gold. Do I not rule over this great land with wealth enough without you to be called one of Ireland's great queens? I have heard them say that you are no more than a kept man really, husband dear."

Ailill rose from the bed and began to buckle on his sword.

"That is not the truth and well you know it, woman. I have brought you great wealth."

Maeve rose also, and pulled her sword towards her.

"Well, then, prove it—let us each count our wealth and see who is the richest."

"Let us do that, so," said Ailill.

The counting of the goods took many days. First of all, the household goods were piled in great heaps and counted—everything from buckets and tubs to golden rings and bracelets; clothes of all colours; slaves and servants; swords and shields and bronze-tipped spears. But Ailill and Maeve were equal in all that their households held.

Then they started on the animals—the pigs, the sheep, the rams, the lambs, the mares and foals and stallions—but again there was no difference between what they possessed.

Finally, they counted the herds of cattle. They walked around the stockades listening to the bellowing within while all the calves and cows and bulls were counted. And once again, they were equal—except for one thing. Ailill had the great bull Finnbheannach, who had left his wife's herd to be with that of the king.

Maeve's pale face went white with rage when she saw that her husband had something that she did not have, for truly the beast was magnificent. Fifty young boys could play on the breadth of his back, and when he stamped the earth, he dug a trench of thirty feet. The very palace of Cruachain shook when he bellowed.

Maeve felt all her pleasure in her wealth turn to ashes in her mouth, and she demanded of her counsellors where she might find a bull the equal of Finnbheannach. She was told of such a one, the Donn of Cooley, who was owned by the farmer Dáire. She called her messenger, Mac Roth, to her. "Go to Dáire," she said. "And tell him that in exchange for the loan of his bull for a year, I will give him such gifts as he will never have seen before—bondmaids and gold, cattle and horses, and my protection for life. Promise him anything, but come back with the bull."

Mac Roth returned some days later, but without the bull. Maeve came to meet him in her chariot, her face set with anger when she saw no sign of the Donn.

Mac Roth stood before Maeve with his eyes cast down and told his tale: "When we arrived at the house of Dáire, we were welcomed with much honour. I put forward your proposition and the farmer, who is an excitable man, was so delighted that he burst his cushion underneath him, bouncing up and down with glee. He called for wine and fine food to seal the bargain."

Mac Roth paused, then continued in a lower voice. "Some of the company drank too deeply of the good wine put before us. Their tongues were loosened and they began to boast that it was as well Dáire had agreed to let us have the bull, as if he had not done so, it would have been no difficulty for us to take the Donn away from him by force.

"By this stage, Dáire too had been drinking; and he became angry. He told us to go back to our mistress and tell her that he would let no bull of his stray into Connacht." Mac Roth paused.

"Continue," said Maeve icily.

"He said also ..." Mac Roth swallowed. "He said to me to tell my mistress that if she is in need of a bull let her come to him and see what the men of Ulster can do for her."

Maeve's face was set with rage.

"So be it," she said. "We will go to Ulster. We will go into Ulster with such a hosting that the men of Ulster will bow down before us in terror. We have Fergus Mac Róich and he will lead us through the gap of the north and we will slaughter every mother's son of them. I will call on all my allies from the south and the east and we will make these proud Ulstermen eat their words. And then we will take this bull into Connacht to be part of my herd."

She stopped, for she had suddenly noticed that there was a girl sitting in her chariot—a golden-haired girl, armed with a spear and dressed in a speckled green cloak. The girl had not been there the moment before.

Maeve spoke quietly, for she knew by the triple irises in the girl's eyes that she was in the presence of a member of the Sídh. "Who are you?" she asked.

"I am Fedelm the prophetess," the girl answered.

"Tell me then," said Maeve. "Do you see a great victory for me over the Ulstermen?"

The girl's eyes met Maeve's.

"I see crimson; I see red," she said.

"But do you see me bringing the Donn back to my herds?"

"I see crimson; I see red," said the girl again.

"Do you see me leading my army, victorious and proud?"

"I see crimson; I see red," said the girl.

So Maeve turned from her and asked her no more, but began to plan how she would gain allies. She would promise gold and riches, land and bondmaids to those who fought with her, and if that was not enough, she would promise her daughter, Fionnabhair, to the warriors of Ireland. She would even promise her own body to those who would work with her to destroy the forces of Ulster, to beat every warrior of the north into the ground. She would win such a victory that all who heard her story would say that she was the greatest ruler in Ireland. She planned how she would watch, laughing, while Dáire, who had dared to insult her, had his head and his privates cut off and placed on a stake. She counted her finger rings and thought about how many more she could pile in her coffers. She had long ago given up wearing an extra one for every king killed, for there had been so many, but she would be sure to get more to store for her daughter's dowry. She sniffed the air, smelling blood, and watched as a scald-crow took flight from the body of a dead calf, its black shape cutting through the gentle blue sky.

And so began the *Táin Bó Cuailgne*, The Cattle Raid of Cooley.

The story of the Táin *is continued in "The Fight at the Ford" and "The Battle of the Bulls."*

Ardagh Hill, Longford

BRUIDEN BRÍ LÉITH

The *Brú of Midhir* is Ardagh Hill, otherwise known as Slieve Golry or Slieve Callery—a word that comes from Calraighe, the name of one of the ancient tribes which inhabited the area. It is a partially forested hill near the village of Ardagh, County Longford. This is the heart of the midlands—a place of small villages and reasonably good farmland, but prone to flooding in the winter months; some fields remain under water for weeks on end. It is not a place of great dramatic beauty; nor is it a place where much is made of a glorious past. However, this is also the ancient Plain of Tethbha, and Ardagh Hill, rising to no more than 198 metres (650 feet), dominates the surrounding flat area. *Bruiden Brí Léith* means the "Dwelling Place of Liath."

Above: *Ardagh Church, also known as St. Mel's Cathedral, County Longford.*

This hill was the site of the main dwelling of Midhir of the Sídh. Midhir was a wise judge, the foster-father of Aonghus Óg, god of love, and the father of the war-goddess, Macha. His *sídh* was said to be guarded by three cranes, which had only to look on warriors in order to rob them of the will to fight. There are no obvious remains of the *sídh* on Ardagh Hill, and the locals seem more interested in promoting the Oliver Goldsmith connection of the village than its association with one of the more complex and beautiful of the love stories of Ireland—*The Wooing of Étaín.*

The village itself is an unusually pretty one, with rows of well-kept stone cottages, and a sense of an orderly, almost eighteenth-century existence. The ancient cathedral, St. Mel's, which is associated with St. Patrick, stands in the grounds of the Church of Ireland church. St. Mel and his sister, Eiche, both founded monasteries in the area; Eiche was reputed to have been able to carry hot coal in her apron as a sign of her purity—a tradition later attributed to St. Brighid, who also has strong associations with the area. According to Patrick Logan in *The Holy Wells of Ireland*, there is a legend of three nuns with a big spotted cow being seen near Brighid's well at Ardagh.

Legends associated with Ardagh Hill were collected by the Folklore Commission in the 1930s, and many of them are recorded in Máire Mac Neill's book, *The Festival of Lughnasa*. Midhir lives on in these traditions, as the "giant" Midas, who lives in the centre of the hill in a great palace. Unwary children, collecting bilberries here on Lughnasa Sunday at the beginning of August, were warned not too stray to far from their friends as they might fall down the giant's "swallyhole" and never be seen again. In one tale, the giant took his revenge on the foolish individual who tried to quarry the hill by piling sods and stones onto him. Perhaps the most moving story is that of the man who got lost while crossing the hill one night. When his companions searched for him, they found only a flat stone, with blue flowers and grass around it, quite unlike anything else that grew on the hill. For thirty years, these strange flowers grew around the stone, until one day, at a time when the lost man would have been about seventy years of age, they disappeared. Many said that the man had been living under the hill for all that time, sending signs to the upper air, but was now dead. However, the hill was associated not only with disappearances and death, but also with lovers—on Bilberry Sunday, the last Sunday in July, young people gathered the berries and celebrated on the hillside, and the fruit was used to make a special wine which was supposed to act as an aphrodisiac—linking the hill once again with one of the most powerful of the ancient Irish love stories.

The hill is a little outside the town, and much of the ascent can be made by car. From high on its sides, there are panoramic views of the surrounding countryside, but the hill itself seems remote from the village and from the farmland surrounding it. Close by is Frewin Hill, or Dún Fremu, the *dún* of Eochaidh, the Horse King, the Ploughman and the human lover of Étaín. Here he retired, troubled in mind, when Midhir played his final trick on his human vanity and he lost the fair Étaín forever.

The famous Ardagh Chalice has no association with the village—it was found in a place in Limerick of the same name. The hidden gold in Ardagh Hill is not that of metal. In the forest, light flickers through green leaves, and reflects in the pools and peat streams of the hillside. As it flows down through the trees, the water seems to capture the late afternoon sun, shining gold. That gold is all that remains of the hair of Étaín, as she stood on the green in front of Brí Léith on a May morning and waited for her story to begin once again.

THE FINDING OF ÉTAÍN

The great feast of Samhain, the beginning of winter and of the new year, was being celebrated at Tara, and Eochaidh Áireamh, the new high king, had brought a bride to celebrate with him. She was Étaín, the daughter of Étar. Eochaidh Áireamh had searched high and low to find the loveliest and most virtuous of women to become his wife, and when he had come to the pool at Brí Léith, where Étaín was standing with her long, golden hair unbound as she washed herself in a silver basin, he knew that his journey was over. The poets had already made a song about the meeting—telling of Étaín's skin as white and as soft as snow, her cheeks as red as the foxglove, her side long and slender, her eyes the colour of hyacinths and her eyebrows and lashes the blue-black of the beetle's shell. The ladies in the court looked on her with envy but not with hatred, for it was impossible to hate someone so still, so calm—a pool of water that reflected only sunlight.

However, in the midst of all the celebrations, there was one who looked on in agony. This was the king's brother, Ailill Anghubha, who had fallen so much in love with Étaín that he could look at no one else while she was in the room. His love was such that he fell into a terrible sickness, and the druids and the healers could do nothing for him. Eochaidh loved his brother, and although he had to leave the court to make his progress through the country, he said to Étaín, "While I am gone, be sure to look after my brother Ailill; anything he needs to help him recover, make sure that he has it. And if he should die—the gods forbid it—make sure that he is buried with the proper ceremonies of a prince."

It did not take long for Étaín to discover the reason for Ailill's sickness, and, out of a desire to heal him, she agreed to come to his bed one morning. She left the palace at dawn and made her way to the trysting spot, and when she arrived there, she found a man who looked like Ailill. Yet somehow she knew that it was not he. So she turned and left the man without speaking. This happened again the next day and the next, and on the third day, she challenged the man, saying, "Who are you, and what right have you to come to meet me here, stranger?"

At this, the man no longer looked like dark-eyed Ailill, but took the form of a tall, fair-haired young warrior with burning grey eyes and a noble appearance.

"No stranger I am to you, fair one, and my rights to be with you are greater than those of Eochaidh," he said. "I am your husband from your past life in the fairy mounds. Midhir of Brí Léith am I; and sit yourself down, while I tell you the tale that you do not remember."

Étaín could not deny that there was something that seemed familiar about Midhir; so she sat down on the grass in the early sunlight and listened quietly while he told his story. By its end, the birds were singing and it was full light, and small memories were coming back to Étaín: of a place of such beauty that it made the breath catch in her throat; of hunts and feasts and music and glorious troops, of immortal lords and ladies.

"You were born Étaín, the daughter of King Étar of Echrad, the loveliest lady of the Sídh. Many tasks did my brother Aonghus perform in order to win you for me. We lived happily in Brí Léith, until my first wife, Fuamnach, became jealous of my love for you. As I held you in my arms one day, I felt you change, soften, fall from between my fingers—she had transformed you into a pool of water; I caught the pool in a silver bowl. That same water I kept in the sun of my chamber, until out of it came a tiny worm, which in turn grew into a marvellous butterfly, with multi-coloured wings—wings the colour of your eyes and hair and lips and black brows. The fly stayed at my side always until my wife sent a wind to blow you away, over the ocean; you were beaten by winds and storms, until finally you found your way back to Brú na Bóinne, where Aonghus kept you safe in a sunny tower of glass. But again you were driven out by the jealousy of Fuamnach, and blown overland until you fell into the cup of King Étar's wife. She drank you down, and nine months later, Étaín, you were born again to live a new life, as fair and as gentle as you ever were. So will you come to me, away to my palace, back to your own people, away from the griefs of humankind? Will you come to live in bliss once more?"

Étaín thought for a moment.

"Is Fuamnach still there?" she asked.

Midhir laughed and shook his head. "No, she has left me; you would be my one true wife, queen of Brí Léith, where winter never comes and no harsh words are spoken."

Étaín thought again: "I will go with you, for it seems that I remember things now I did not know were part of my memories; but I will go only with the consent of Eochaidh, for I would not set up dissent between him and the people of the Sídh."

Midhir bowed deeply and said, "So shall it be, lady—I will win you from Eochaidh."

When Étaín went back to Ailill, she found him cured of his sickness. He said that each dawn, when he had tried to go to meet her, he had been overcome with a great tiredness, unable to move. However, now he no longer felt the madness of longing for her, and they could tell the king what had happened. Eochaidh was pleased with the care Étaín had shown for his brother, and Ailill took the name of Ailill One-Stain, for the only bad deed he had committed was to love his brother's wife. Étaín said nothing to her husband about Midhir's promise.

At Bealtaine, the beginning of summer, a tall, grey-eyed warrior appeared before Eochaidh and challenged him to a game of chess. At first, Eochaidh refused, saying that the board was in his wife's chamber and that he did not wish to disturb her, but Midhir—for it was he—produced a wonder from his bag—golden pieces and a silver board, and they sat down to play.

Eochaidh won every game, and, as a payment, he demanded that Midhir perform many great tasks including to clear the rocks and stones from the plains of Meath, so that, from that day, cattle could graze on the most fertile land of Ireland; and to cut down great forests and remove the rushes around his palace of Tethbha. Finally, he asked Midhir to build a causeway over the bog of Lamrach. Midhir completed all these tasks, but he stipulated that none should watch him while the tasks were done. Eochaidh's steward, however, watched the ploughing of the land for the causeway, and, the next day, when the task was completed, Midhir came angrily to Eochaidh.

"You have broken your pledge," he said. "None was to watch while I worked for you. You are a man of no honour and you are not worthy of the great gifts you have been given. I demand the right of one last game."

The king looked around at his soldiers—should he call them in to overcome this impudent man who dared to criticise the king? Then he thought of the deeds that Midhir had done—the great magical forces at his command, and he looked to where his wife was standing, watching him, expecting him to do the honourable thing. He nodded.

This time the game went very differently—within nine moves, the king was defeated. He held up his hands and asked, "What is your prize, then, warrior?"

"I ask for a kiss from the fair Étaín," replied Midhir.

Eochaidh went pale. He was silent for a time, furious with himself—for is it not always the case with a wager that it should demand the thing most beloved of the loser? Finally, he said, "Very well. Come back in one month for the payment of the debt."

When Midhir came back the following month, the palace was surrounded by legions of soldiers from every corner of Ireland—all there to ensure that Midhir would not carry Étaín away with him. But Midhir smiled as he stood before the king, saying, "I have come then, for the kiss from Étaín."

Étaín stepped down from her seat beside the king to where Midhir stood in the centre of the great hall of Tara. Around her on all sides were warriors and ladies and all the people of the court, watching. She cast one half-smiling glance to where Ailill stood, and a final serious one at Eochaidh; then she went into the embrace of Midhir's arms. As she did so, the couple rose above all the assembled company, higher and higher into the air, until they flew through the smoke-hole in the centre of the hall. A great cry rose up from the people and they raced outside. But all they could see were two beautiful white swans flying away in the blue sky, linked by a silver chain around their necks. Eochaidh sat in the hall with his head in his hands, thinking of his lost beloved, and the lost child that she carried within her.

Some say that Midhir and Étaín lived happily from then on, man and wife as they had been fated to be from the dawn of time. However, there are others who say that Eochaidh razed all the fairy palaces in Ireland, searching for his lost bride. It is said that he finally came to Brí Léith, and Étaín, tired of the violence and destruction that the king was inflicting on the Sídh, convinced Midhir to go out to parley. Eochaidh demanded his wife back, and Midhir told him to return in a month when Étaín would go with him.

"But if you are to have her, you must show that you know her, the way that I have always known her through all her transformations. And if you do not know her, you must swear that you will stop the destruction of the *sídh*."

Eochaidh laughed. "Of course I would always know my beloved—her fair head, her white side, her red lips. Your terms hold no terror for me."

When Eochaidh returned, he found fifty women of the exact appearance of Étaín standing in front of him, each smiling the smile of his wife, each speaking in her gentle tones. He looked at each one intently, trying to find something that would mark one of them out as his true wife. But what he had always seen when he looked at his beloved was his own image reflected and magnified in her eyes—and here were fifty maidens, all gazing at him with that same look. Midhir's smile widened and he urged Eochaidh to choose.

Eochaidh stood, watching the maidens, unable to say who was his own Étaín. He asked them questions, but they all seemed to know the answer; he danced with some, but they moved with the same liquid charm as his wife. Finally, he said, "There is one act that no other woman could do with the grace of my wife—I would ask each of these maidens to serve me wine."

So, each maiden took a cup and a jug, and served wine to the king; each one did it with great skill and grace, until all but two had done so. Then one of the last two moved forward, smiling, lifted the jug to pour the wine, and carried it to the hand of the king.

"This is my Étaín," shouted Eochaidh. "This is the one I will take."

Midhir smiled again, and the last remaining woman, with a glance over her shoulder, made her way into the *sídh*. With great rejoicing, Eochaidh brought back Étaín to Tara, and she was soon with child by him. However, one day, as he sat with his wife in his arms, and his new daughter in the cradle beside them, he asked her, "And tell, me, beloved, what happened the first child you bore?"

"This is the first child I have had," said Étaín. "Why, since I was born in the *sídh* at Brí Léith, I have known no other man but you."

Then Eochaidh realised that he had chosen wrongly, and had taken his daughter instead of his wife from the Sídh. In a great rage, he commanded his servants to kill the child that the second Étaín had borne. But the little girl had the beauty and charm that was the gift and curse of all the Étaíns, and, in pity for her and her mother, the servants did not kill her, but instead hid the baby in the forest. There she was found by a cowherd and his wife, and fostered by them in ignorance of her noble birth. In time, this third Étaín, Mes Buachalla the cowherd's fosterling, became the wife of a prince and bore Conaire, who became one of the noblest kings of Ireland. Despite King Conaire's greatness, he too was fated to be punished for his grandfather's destruction of the *sídh* of Ireland—but that is another story.

Conaire's story is told in "Da Dearga's Hostel."

Keshcorann Caves, Sligo

CÉIS CHORAINN

The caves of Keshcorann are easily accessible, located halfway up the western slopes of Keshcorann mountain. They are situated on the road from Ballymote to Boyle, just before the village of Keash. The caves are clearly visible from the main road, and a side road to the left brings you within a short, although very steep, climb to the caves themselves. If you continue the climb up the mountain, you will find a cairn and the remains of a ringfort at its summit. There are seventeen caves and, although very little evidence of human habitation has been found in them (excavations found only the bones of hares, foxes and bears), they are an important site in terms of their legendary associations. The mountain range on which they stand is called the Bricklieves, or Speckled Mountains, and from the slopes of the caves there are fine views over the

surrounding countryside. Some of the caves link into each other, and wet-weather gear is essential for exploring them, as the floor is covered in a heavy brown slush which seems to contain a large percentage of liquefied sheep manure. In one cave to the left of the range, however, the interior is a vivid green world. Here, the rocks are spilt with tiny fronds of fern and psychedelically bright algae.

Keshcorann gets its name from Corann, a poet of the Dé Danann whose music calmed the rampaging sow, Caelchéis (*Céis* means "The Wicker Causeway"). In gratitude for saving the people from the beast, the lands were granted to him, to hold his name forever. This connection with the ancient mythical sow suggests that, as at Ben Bulben, some form of very ancient animal worship or sacrifice may have taken place here. The caves on the hill were one of the resting places of that ubiquitous pair of lovers, Diarmaid and Gráinne, and also the home of the magical smith, Lon Mac Líomtha, the master craftsmen who had only one leg and one eye, but in recompense had three arms. In one of the caves, a she-wolf suckled the infant Cormac in the days before he took up his rightful place as high king of Ireland. Until relatively recently, the caves were visited on Bilberry or Garland Sunday, the last Sunday in July, in an echo of the ancient Lughnasa rite.

On the other side of the mountain is Lough Arrow, the site of the famous Second Battle of Moytura, when the Tuatha Dé Danann defeated the race of the

Fomorians, their rivals for the control of the land of Ireland. Myth and history mingle on the shores of the lake, for this is the location of Carrowkeel, Sligo's second great Megalithic graveyard and ceremonial centre. Carrowkeel is one of the most impressive ancient landscapes in Ireland. Many of the tombs predate Newgrange and may be from as early as 3800BC. The complex contains wedge, passage, portal and court tombs. Pottery from the passage tombs has given its name to a pottery type, Carrowkeel ware.

At the time the Carrowkeel complex was built, the slopes of the hillside at Keshcorann would have been heavily forested in elm, hazel and oak, honeysuckle and holly. Now there is long, slippery grass and a dotting of golden furze and white hawthorn. Sure-footed sheep graze around the caves and the view is over placid, cultivated countryside. This area is a quiet one, with small friendly towns—many, such as Tobercurry, with a strong tradition of Irish music. Near Tobercurry is another famous mountain of the Sídh, Knocknashee. In Castlebaldwin there is an information centre which would make a useful start to any exploration of the area. The countryside here is less dramatic than in north Sligo, and few people visit the caves. When we visited the site on a wet June Sunday, we met only one other person—a writer who had come from Australia because of the myths associated with Keshcorann. For most of the time, the caves are undisturbed, silent places of transformation and mysteries long ago forgotten.

THE HAGS OF WINTER

Fionn, the great warrior and hunter, ran through woods on the steep slopes on Keshcorann, delighting in the brush of branches against his arms and legs, the sharp smell of early winter, the call of the hounds and the shouts of his men. He was bound, he felt, for an adventure, a tale to tell during the long winter evenings around the blazing hearth of Almiu. Only his hounds and his companion, Conán, were with him, for he could still outrun all of the Fianna, even his son and his grandson; the only one to match him on any day was Caoilte Mac Rónáin. However, although the adventure that was about to befall Fionn would be told at many a fireside in years to come, it was not Fionn who would be the hero in it, but the man who would become his bitterest enemy—Goll Mac Morna.

Suddenly, the forest disappeared. A thick mist had come down; the dogs began to whine. The two men forced the hounds onwards, for they had been on the scent of a deer and were determined not to let it escape. But another smell was taking over from the scent of the deer—a smell of darkness and decay. The way up the hill was steep and very slippery underfoot. Fionn fell once and cursed as he tried to wipe off the brown, stinking mud clinging to his knees and hands. As the mist cleared slightly, the two hunters found themselves at the mouth of a cave where the smell grew stronger. Just discernible in the darkness were three old women. Each was uglier than the next; each was misshapen and wrinkled. Each had crimson hair, bristling out like the bristles of a boar; each had a stubbly beard and their black lips hung down to their withered breasts. Worst of all were their eyes. Each one of the six eyes gazing on the warriors was a blank white space, faintly veined with blue, with no iris or pupil. The three creatures were spinning, and as they spun, they hummed. Curious, Fionn and his companion pushed back the holly bush that grew at the mouth of the cave, and made their way inside, calling on the dogs that had hung back behind them, shivering and whining. As they passed the bush, the two men felt a great weakness come upon them and they fell to the ground. The spinners were witches, the daughters of a sorcerer; they were called Camóg, Cuilleann and Iornach. They were set to take revenge on Fionn on behalf of their father, who hated to see the wild things of his woods disturbed by the hunting of the Fianna. The three old women wound the great Fionn and his companion in their threads and they lay there, trussed up like babies, while the hags cackled at each other in victorious joy.

Soon, the rest of the Fianna appeared, drawn to the cave by the howls of Bran and Sceolan, the wise dogs who had refused to enter the enchanted place. When they saw their leader bound and gagged, the Fianna rushed forward into the cave, but they too were overtaken by the magic, and left as weak as kittens, trapped like flies in the spinners' webs. The smiles of the hags became even wider, and they were about to start stringing up the Fianna onto their cooking spits when an almighty bellow came from the mouth of the cave. It was Goll Mac Morna, who had slain Fionn's father and who would, in turn, one day be slain by Fionn. Goll had never lost his loyalty to his companions in arms. Cleverer and older than the rest of the men, he did not put one toe beyond the holly bush, but waved his sword and challenged the hags to battle.

"There's three of us and one of him," said the eldest. "Let's shut him up."

The three witches came forward and set upon Goll like angry hornets, but he spun around with his sword flashing in the weak winter sun, so that,

Opposite:
Entrance to the caves at Keshcorann, County Sligo.

half-blinded, they put their hands to their eyes. In an instant, he had managed to split two of them with one sword-stroke. The third hag was so aghast at losing her sisters that she threw herself down before Goll, promising to remove the enchantment from the Fianna if he spared her life. This he did, and Fionn and the Fianna came from the cave, rubbing their eyes, their legs still shaking. But just at that moment, a fourth sister witch appeared, yowling in rage. In an instant, Goll had lifted his sword again and killed her also.

They left the bodies of the witches at the cave for their father to find, but they took home the young deer that the Fianna had slaughtered.

In gratitude for his rescue, Fionn offered Goll his own daughter, Sgannlach. She was a good wife to Goll, and stayed faithful to her husband even after enmity had broken out again between the two men. The couple were hunted by Fionn the length and breath of Ireland; finally, they ended on a barren rock far out to sea on the west coast, with Fionn on their tail and a great army ready to destroy them. There, far from the fertile valleys and bird-filled forests, Goll begged his wife to leave him and save her own life. But this she refused to do, and so they died, side by side, bound together by ties even stronger than the magic of the witches of Keshcorann.

Ben Bulben, Sligo

BEANN GULBAN

The distinctive, scooped-out edge of Ben Bulben faces out towards the coastline of Sligo and acts as a signature to a county which not only contains a wealth of folklore, archaeology and history but is also rich in stunning natural beauty, encompassing wild sea and high mountain valleys. *Beann Gulban* means "The Mountain Peak of Gulban" but it is not known who or what Gulban was. This countryside is haunted by the ghosts of William Butler Yeats and his brother, Jack, both of whom were possessed by Sligo—its scenery, its folklore and its people—throughout their lives. Reading any of Yeats's poetry—particularly the earlier works—gives one a feeling for Sligo in a way that no prose can, as does looking at a Jack Butler Yeats painting such as *Memory Harbour*.

Above:
An engraving depicting the distinctive outline of Ben Bulben on the horizon.

The ascent of Ben Bulben should be undertaken only by those with good navigational skills, and, as usual in Ireland, mist can come down suddenly, so suitable clothing and footwear should be worn. The top of the mountain is particularly boggy. There are several routes which can be taken to the trig point marking the summit. Unfortunately, one of the most picturesque of these at the Gleniff Horseshoe has most of the routes blocked off by anti-access notices which must be among the most aggressive in Ireland. Those who do make the climb will be rewarded by magnificent views over the surrounding countryside and numerous sightings of what look like caves but which are, in fact, the remains of the workings of the now-defunct Ben Bulben barytes mines, which closed in the late 1970s. The mythical boar of Ben Bulben has had many stories told about it and may be a link to a time when animals were sacrificed as a way of communication with the gods.

Those unwilling or unable to do the climb can find consolation in the drive up to and around the Gleniff Horseshoe—particularly lovely when the evening light comes in from the west—or the less arduous trek to the top of Knocknarea, where the gigantic cairn is said to cover the grave of Queen Maeve. Not far away from the cairn is the Carrowmore complex of tombs, which is possibly the oldest in the country. It is estimated that some of the monuments in the huge complex date from as early as 4000BC. Unfortunately, many of the original 60 monuments were destroyed—some, even more unfortunately, by careless early excavation. Despite this, it is a unique experience to walk through a landscape filled with strange humps and lumps, which turn out to be cairns and tombs. Houses and fields mingle in among the relics of ancient days, and the line between ancient past and the present blurs. No wonder Sligo was such a rich ground for stories of the Sídh—the other world literally rises up before you on every side.

Some of the tombs, such as Listoghil, are now part of land owned by Dúchas, and there is a good interpretative centre where you can buy a map of the site. Like Rathcroghan, this is a place where it is well worth while giving yourself plenty of time to wander around. Part of the joy of the experience is that this can be done without being surrounded by crowds of people. The only groups that you are likely to meet are the assemblies of ancient stones, which from a distance can seem like the backs of grey-cloaked men and women, huddled together for a gossip that has lasted thousands of years.

THE STORY OF DIARMAID AND GRÁINNE

Cormac Mac Airt sat in his hall with his head in his hands. Despite his reputation as the wisest king Ireland had ever known, he had no idea what to do. His problem was his youngest daughter, Gráinne—a girl as fair as a lily but as wild as a hare. No scoldings from her mother nor threats from her father could stop her from eyeing up the warriors as they practised on the green at Tara, and he was afraid that she would present him with a grandchild before he could marry her off to a prince, making her another man's problem. He groaned slightly, and the old warrior Fionn, who was sitting opposite him, asked him if he had had too much wine the previous night.

"It's not my head that is my problem," said Cormac. "It's that child of mine, Gráinne. I need to get her married off quickly before she disgraces me with some stable-boy."

Fionn put down his drink and looked speculatively at his high king. "Gráinne is the blonde one, isn't she?" he asked. "She's a fine girl."

"Ah, she's lovely enough," said Cormac. "But she has a will like iron. No young man can get the better of her tongue."

Fionn smiled slightly. "Well, if no young man can manage her, why not try for a not-so-young one?" he suggested. "A man with years of experience of dealing with the female sex."

Now Cormac put down his cup also. "And would you be thinking of anyone in particular?" he asked.

So it was agreed that Gráinne should marry Fionn, and, strangely enough, when her father broke the news to her, she did not scream and roar as she had at any of the other suggestions he had put to her. Maybe, he thought to himself, the pot-bellied old boaster was right, and an older man would suit his headstrong daughter.

Perhaps Gráinne had been misled by the stories of Fionn's prowess into thinking that he was still a young and handsome warrior. In any case, when she saw the grizzled and hoary man that she was to marry, her face dropped. And what is also certain is that the night before the wedding, Gráinne disappeared with the flower of the Fianna, and one of Fionn's most beloved warriors, Diarmaid Ua Duibhne, Diarmaid of the Lovespot.

Opposite: *A wintery view of Ben Bulben.*

Fionn was furious when he awoke at noon to find his head aching and his bride fled. Like himself, all of the Fianna, with the exception of Oisín and Oscar, had been put into an enchanted sleep by a draught from Gráinne's

hand. It did not help his mood when Oisín told him that Gráinne had originally suggested that he himself become her lover.

"You are well shot of her, my father," he said. "She will lead poor Diarmaid a merry dance, for although she is beautiful, he did not want to go with her at all. But she mocked him and then put a *geis* upon him, so he had no choice. She caught him like a rabbit in the trap of his own honour."

However, Fionn had been looking forward to bedding Gráinne. Moreover, he hated to be crossed by anyone, so that, even more than lust, anger drove him, and hatred, fuelled by the fear that his powers were failing and that the young lovers had made a fool of him. He began the great hunt for Diarmaid and Gráinne which would lead the Fianna all over Ireland.

When Diarmaid and Gráinne left Tara, they went west of the Shannon, and then southwards towards Slieve Luachra. Always, Fionn pursued them, though his greatest warriors, Oscar, Oisín and Caoilte, held their companion Diarmaid in such affection that they hindered rather than helped Fionn in his angry quest. The lovers could never eat where they cooked nor sleep where they ate. They were pursued through forests and over mountainsides, onto islands and through bogs. They knew the freezing cold of winter and the relentless sun of midsummer. Ireland is marked with hundreds of dolmens called "The Bed of Diarmaid and Gráinne."

All the time they travelled, Diarmaid refused to betray Fionn by making love to Gráinne, though she did not make it easy for him; for while she had thought him handsome when she saw him in the banqueting hall, the trials that they went through together made her truly love him as well as desire him. Every night, Diarmaid would put a fishbone between himself and Gráinne as they slept, so that if one of them rolled over towards the other it would stick into them and keep them apart. Then, one spring day, after Diarmaid had fought his way through an army of the Fianna and they had made their way over a mountain stream, Gráinne stood on the bank and mocked Diarmaid as he pulled back the hawthorn for her to make her way into the safety of the thicket.

"Look, Diarmaid Ua Duibhne, you who are called the great lover of the Fianna. Look how the water has splashed up onto my thigh. Despite all your courage in battle, that water is braver than you in terms of where it dares to go."

Then Diarmaid, who had desired Gráinne for many months, pulled her into the thicket and he made love to her; and he let Fionn know by secret signs that he had done so.

So the lovers' adventures continued for sixteen years, with the pair sleeping in bothies in the green woods and living off the nuts and fruits of the land. Winter followed summer, and always they moved on, unable to rest for fear of Fionn. Sometimes, Gráinne would sleep on rushes, and Diarmaid on sea-sand, so that Fionn's magic thumb would not be able to tell him whether they were on the mountainside or the seashore. They had friends in their wanderings, especially Aonghus, the god of love, who was foster-father of Diarmaid, and loved him like his own child. It was he who finally made peace between the exiles and Fionn. It was agreed that Diarmaid and Gráinne should live far from Fionn and the Fianna in Sligo; but although Fionn pretended to have forgiven the lovers, he bided his time and waited for revenge. Fionn never gave up the hunt.

One fine summer's morning, Diarmaid awoke after a restless night and said that he would go hunting on Ben Bulben.

"Do not go, my love," said Gráinne. "For I fear for you—you were calling out in your sleep and I am afraid that your dreams mean that something evil will befall you. And besides, I would like you to help me with some work in the house."

However, over the years, Diarmaid had learned how to ignore Gráinne. He left the house with his spear and his hound. He climbed the great flank of the mountain, and, near the top, he came upon Fionn, sitting on a hillock. His face had become fleshy over the years, his eyes small and mean, but he was smiling. Diarmaid knew that smile of old—it was the one that Fionn always wore just before he put his spear through the heart of a deer after a long day's hunting.

"Well, old companion," said Fionn. "You have picked a good day for the chase, for the wild boar of Ben Bulben has been seen out on the hillside today." He sighed. "But of course it is not up to you to hunt it, for is there not a *geis* on you not to kill a pig? And I am sure that your wife would not like it if you took such risks. How is the lovely Gráinne?"

Diarmaid said quietly, "Gráinne is as lovely as ever. But do not tell me where or what I can hunt. I have never turned back from the chase yet." And he left Fionn and began to search for the boar's tracks.

He heard it before he saw it, rampaging through the gorse, snorting its fury. It appeared through the brushwood, its hide as thick as iron, its cruel tusks and angry red eyes squinting as it came into the sunshine. Diarmaid ran towards it, sinking his spear into its flank, as his hound tried to dig its teeth into its thick hide. The beast threw off the great hound as if it were no more than a fly, and the dog fell onto its back yards away, whimpering miserably. But Diarmaid's spear had gored the creature's skin and now he held it fast.

The great beast ran all over the slopes of the mountain, trying to buck Diarmaid off his back. So it went on, with Diarmaid hanging on for dear life, sometimes wrestling the boar with his arms caught around its neck like a lover, sometimes just barely holding on to the end of his spear as the creature dragged him through gorse and heather and bracken and scrub, up and down the steep mountainside. Finally, the boar gave a massive buck, and Diarmaid fell on the earth. The beast dug one of its tusks into his tormentor's flesh, goring his belly from hip to shoulder. Diarmaid lay there and, with one last burst of strength, pushed the hilt of his sword deep into the boar's belly. The beast fell, dead from battle wounds and exhaustion. Nearby, Fionn sat saying nothing. By now, the rest of the Fianna had arrived, and Oisín said angrily to his father: "Do something now, for Diarmaid, our dear companion of old, is near death. You know that you can cure anyone, no matter how badly wounded, with a drink from your hands."

Fionn strolled over to where Diarmaid was lying in agony.

"Not looking so well now, are you, Diarmaid, beloved of women? Of course, I'd love to help, but I'm only an oul' fella with bad eyesight. I can see no water near here."

Diarmaid groaned, "I have seen a fresh stream no more than a few feet away, Fionn; and for the gods' sake, help me, for I have always been a faithful friend to you. It was only because Gráinne put a *geis* on me that I went with her, as you well know. And it was so long ago...I know you have planned this; but have mercy now and save my life."

"And what about the kisses you gave to her in front of me and my men when I found you? And your life with her and the children she bore you—are not these a mockery of me?"

Fionn stood staring down at Diarmaid, but Oisín came up and shook his father's shoulders, shouting, "Old man, if you do not go now and get water for Diarmaid, I will kill you with my own hands. You know that we cannot let a companion die like this. Go to him now!"

Fionn shrugged. He went slowly to the pool and filled his cupped hands with water, but when he drew near to Diarmaid, and saw how handsome he still was, and thought of how he and young Gráinne had made a fool and a cuckold of him for so many years, he let the water trickle through his fingers.

Twice he went to the well and took water in his hands to bring to Diarmaid, but twice, as he returned to where the hero was lying, his jealous memories got the better of him and he let it pour to the ground.

Oisín was shouting at his father now, telling him to move quickly and help the dying man who was lying in his arms, shaking uncontrollably. So, finally, Fionn took the water all the way to where Diarmaid was lying. But at that moment, the hero died.

Gráinne gave a great cry of pain when she saw the Fianna returning from the mountain with Diarmaid's hound limping beside them and a body carried on a bier made of green branches. For years, she planned a revenge on Fionn, training her children in the ways of battle. When Fionn heard of this, he came to her, and, in spite of all the slights and insults she piled on him, he stayed with her, calling her his honey tongue, his sweetheart, until one day she looked in the mirror and saw that although Fionn was an old man, she herself was no longer young. And she thought that although she would never love anyone as she had loved Diarmaid, there was a lot to be said for being the wife of a great leader. She knew that even though Fionn was silver-haired and red-faced, he was reputed to be a great lover, so that even the fairy-women came out of the *sídh* to sleep with him. Finally, she went with him to Almiu.

When the couple arrived at Almiu, the Fianna, whom Fionn had commanded to come out to greet his bride, shouted out their derision. They called to Fionn to mind his wife well this time, so that Gráinne dropped her head in shame. But she held it up again when she saw the rich robes and jewels prepared for her, the servants ready to do her bidding, and the lordly bed with its red silk hangings, so different from the bothy of branches she had slept in when she had run away in her wild youth with sweet-lipped Diarmaid Ua Duibhne.

ULSTER

Grianán of Aileach, Donegal

GRIANÁN AILIGH

The Grianán—or sun-palace—of Aileach is a circular stone enclosure, a cashel, situated 244 metres (800 feet) above sea level and visible from miles around. It is easily accessible, as a road leads to the top of the hill on which it is situated. Around the massive stone enclosure, with its single entrance leading through the thick walls, there are three concentric earthen banks. The Grianán was built on the site of an ancient tumulus which may date from Neolithic times—it was certainly already in place by the Bronze Age. The present structure probably dates from the Iron Age, and was heavily restored in the nineteenth century. The edifice is an impressive one, and the surrounding views are staggering, stretching over five counties and encompassing mountains, lakes, beaches, cliffs, pastureland, the loughs Swilly and Foyle and the wild Atlantic. Derry, St. Colmcille's city where it was said that the angels were as numerous as the leaves on the oak trees, can be clearly seen to the southeast.

This is the centre of one of the ancient kingdoms of Ulster, and kings were ceremoniously crowned at Aileach until the twelfth century. The Uí Néills in the fifth century and later the O'Donnells reigned from here. Inside the cashel, there is relief from the howling presence of the wind, and smooth, green grass, with the layered walls rising in a circle around the inner court. The place acted as sanctuary, as an inaugural centre and as a palace. It was said that in its heyday the building was covered in red yew, in gold and bronze and in precious stones so that it shone as brightly in the day as in the night. Outside the cashel are the remains of an ancient roadway and a holy well.

The Grianán was the target of attack from the enemies of the king, notably the Danes in 937. After 1101, it was no longer used as a royal residence, having been destroyed by Murtagh O'Brien, the king of Munster. In revenge for the destruction of Kincora in 1088, Murtagh was said to have told his troops to take a stone each from the structure, so that it could never be rebuilt. The Grianán was, however, used again—not by the nobility of the land but by the peasantry in the eighteenth century, who took shelter in it to attend forbidden masses.

There are many legends associated with the Grianán—particularly in relation to the building of the palace. Some say that the great Daghdha himself built the original structure. Others say that, in the fourth century, a master-builder called Friguan eloped with the daughter of the king of Scotland and built the sun-palace in her name. There is a further association with St. Patrick, who is said to have baptised King Eoghan here. Of more recent date is a folktale which associates the site with the Irish hero, Hugh O'Donnell. It is said that a man passed over the hill of the Grianán one night and saw a bright light shining from it. When he looked inside the light, he saw a great company of horsemen with swords and shields and shining armour. They sat upright on their horses, yet seemed to be sleeping. One of them opened his eyes and said to the man, "Is it time yet?" holding his horn to the ready. The man ran away in terror, knowing that what he had seen was the sleeping company of Hugh O'Donnell, waiting for the moment to come to do battle for the land.

Pages 180-181:
W.H. Bartlett's engraving of "Dunseverick Castle," standing on the ancient site of Dún Sobhairce, one of the four royal roads which led from Tara.

THE GODS OF THE HILL

The Daghdha, the Lord of Plenty and the great builder, sat strumming his harp as he looked over the northern ocean. Behind him was the Grianán, the sun-palace of Aileach. It was almost completed, this work of giants, and the great mother Danu would be pleased, for here was a fitting residence for the shining ones. The Daghdha was satisfied because he knew that his work would last well beyond even his long reign as All-Father of the Tuatha Dé Danann. Feasts would be held here, celebrations of Samhain and Bealtaine, contests and races and tourneys. The children of the Sídh would be born here, and grow to adulthood, and live out their thousands of years. All would move in an ordered pattern, like planets in their allotted spheres. He himself would be the great gift-giver and protector; Manannán would rule the kingdom of the sea; Áine the sun; Donn, the gentle king, the shadowlands of the dead; Brighid the flocks and the wild things; Eochaidh the herds of swift horses; and Lugh would be their many-skilled defender and their king. Even those other ones, those who were less kindly but still part of the immortal family—the Morrigan and her sisters, Badbh and Macha—had their part to play.

The Daghdha's smile grew broader—truly, his mating with the Morrigan had been a magnificent one, as she had stood with one foot on either side of the River Uinsinn. He prided himself that he could fill a woman's womb as well as his cauldron could fill a belly—leaving none dissatisfied. And her assistance at the battle had been a decisive element in their great victory. The children of Danu had finally defeated the evil Fomorians at the Battle of the Plain of the Two Pillars, Moytura.

Now the song that he played told the story of that struggle—of how the shining ones had driven the forces of darkness from the land. The battle had been long coming and hard fought. Years before, the Tuatha Dé Danann had fought the Fomorians and defeated them. But during that battle, the great leader, Nuadhu, had lost his arm and had thus had to give up the kingship, for the leader of the realm had to be without blemish. Bres, half Fomorian and half of the race of the Tuatha Dé Danann, had become the new king, but he had been a tyrant, forcing the gods into slavery and conniving with the Fomorians, especially with the giant, Balor na Súile Nimhe (Balor of the Evil Eye). The Daghdha sang of how the physician, Dian Céacht, had made a new arm of shining silver for Nuadhu, and he had taken back the kingship of the

Above:
The sun sets over the Grianán of Aileach, County Donegal.

Tuatha Dé Danann, and the leaders had met and decided to finish the fight with their enemies for once and for all.

The Daghdha sang of the preparations for the second great battle, when, led by Nuadhu, the smiths and wrights and carpenters had forged magical weapons and built battle-chariots. He sang of the death of Nuadhu, and of how the shining Lugh of the Long Arm had killed his grandfather, Balor, with a stone from his sling shot through the giant's malevolent eye. He sang of how Goibhniu the smith had made magical weapons that mended themselves overnight, however badly they were broken during the battle, and how Dian Cécht had cured those who had been wounded. He sang of how the Fomorians and their allies, the Fir Bolg, had been routed and had fled to their ships, and how the body of Nuadhu of the Silver Arm had been taken to Grianán. He was now buried under the great stone enclosure, and the hero, Lugh, had taken his place as king of the tribe of Danu.

Finally, the Daghdha sang of how his days of servitude to the Fomorians were over. Now he could concentrate on what he wanted to do, on what he did best—building great palaces that would last for as long as there was life in Ireland. The treasures of the Tuatha Dé Danann would be kept there—those treasures taken from the four magical cities in the north of the world—the sword of Nuadhu, the spear of Lugh, the stone of Fál and his own cauldron, which was never emptied no matter how many were fed. There was no reason why the Dé Danann should ever give up their hold on this green and fertile land.

He continued his song, and did not see the sails that were coming over the horizon from the lands to the east; nor did he hear the calls of the Sons of Míl as they came nearer to the mountainous shores far to the south of Aileach. Despite the enchantments of the Tuatha Dé Danann, who had covered the shores of their island in a magic mist so that no one should find it, a new race had seen the land of Ireland and coveted its beauty. The Daghdha, great as he was, did not foresee that the children of Danu would be banished to the world under the green hills, hidden from human sight. Despite his power and wisdom, he did not hear the song the Sons of Míl sang as their sages landed—a song invoking a power older and greater even than that of the children of Danu. As their small crafts scraped onto the shingle, the Milesians called on the land of Ireland itself—its forests, its rivers, its hills and its lakes, its broad plains and forested glens—to welcome a new tribe to its shores.

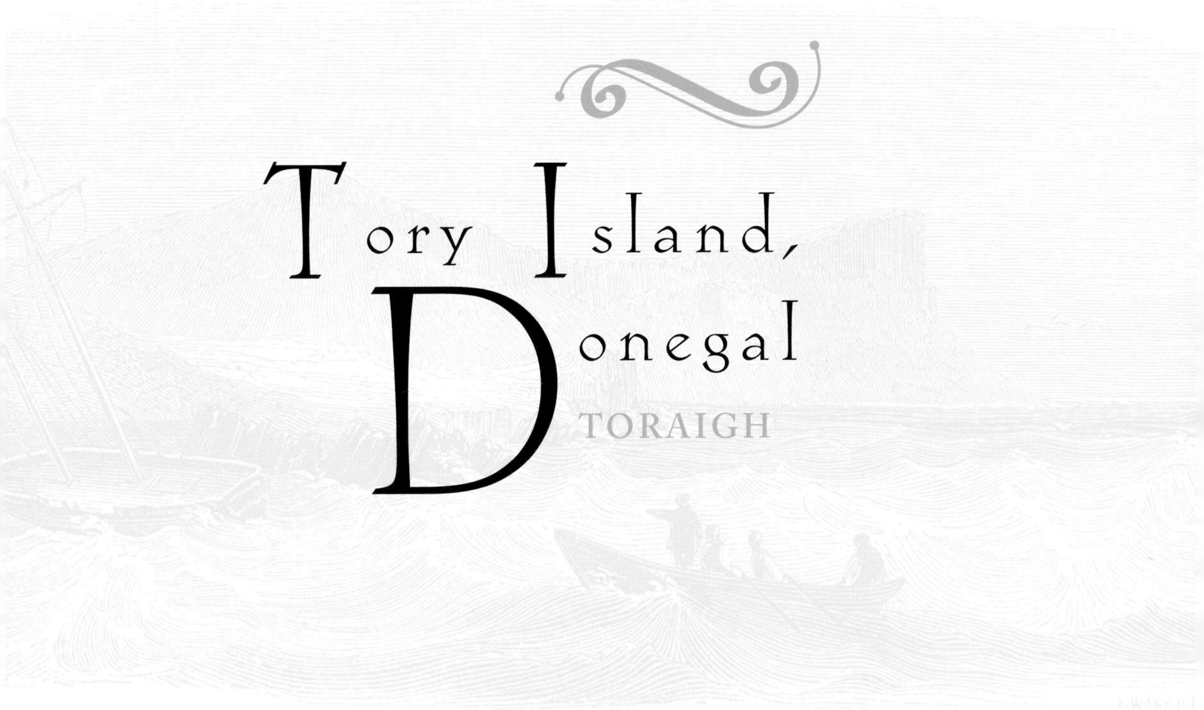

Tory Island, Donegal

TORAIGH

There is a traditional Irish dance called "The Waves of Tory." It is a fast-moving, communal dance, which can get pretty wild late at night at a *ceilí*. The wilder it gets, the closer it comes to its name, for the waves of Tory have to be experienced to be believed. Tory Island is the most isolated of the inhabited islands off the coast of Ireland, not because of distance—it is no more than 12 kilometres (7 miles) away from the nearest point on the Irish coast—but because of the wildness of the seas which separate it from the mainland. Because of this isolation, the people of Tory have always been a race apart—indeed, one translation of the name Tory links it to the Irish word for pirates. The most commonly accepted interpretation of its name, however, is that Tory means "Towery Place," and, approaching the island's distinctive profile from the sea does give one the feeling of moving towards a battlemented fortress.

As recently as the middle of the 1980s, there were plans to evacuate the island and relocate the remaining families on the mainland—this was after the winter of 1974 when the island was cut off from the mainland for over seven weeks. The people of Tory fought back, however, and now the island has a regular ferry service, plans for a small airport, and a thriving school of local artists. It is also an island whose people have fiercely guarded its traditions, its music, its monuments and its folklore.

The island is 5 kilometres (3 miles) long and at its widest no more than 1 kilometre (half a mile) wide—in places, it is much narrower. It is bare and treeless, made up mainly of rock and bog, with some pasture lands. Despite this, it manages to support a variety of bird life, including water birds such as swans, and sea birds such as puffins and gannets. In summer, it is also the home of the now rare corncrake—in the evenings, their rasping calls from the low hedges and long grass make it seem as if Tory itself is calling out. The island is never silent—between the calls of the birds and the noise of the wind and the sea, there is a feeling of ceaseless movement and turbulence.

The turbulence is reflected in the folklore, for the island was the fortress of the great giant, Balor na Súile Nimhe (Balor of the Evil Eye)—the greedy and merciless giant who could murder with a glance. Balor's Soldiers (also called the Eochair Mhór) are the sea cliffs which form a line of serrated rock on the northeast of the island, some distance out to sea. Directly aligned with the coast, they act as a second rocky wall of defence for the island at this point in the coastline. This is the

highest point of the island, and here its beauty is harsh and uncompromising—unsoftened by any greenery. This peninsula forms the area known as Balor's Fort, and there are the remaining traces of an Iron Age promontory fort. Four embankments acted as defence from the rest of the peninsula, and the remains of a well and twenty huts have been found here by archaeologists.

The most obvious archaeological remains on the island are, however, the Christian ones. Legend has it that St. Colmcille, Donegal's patron saint and the founder of Iona, founded a monastery here, which flourished for a thousand years—from the sixth to the sixteenth century. There are many legends concerning St. Colmcille's deeds on the island, and there are still impressive remains of a round tower and an unusual Tau or T-cross. Other remains include the bed of the holy woman whose body was washed up on the island—clay from this site is still said to contain magical properties. Parts of the island's magical heritage were less benign. It is said that the cursing stone, now hidden away from human use, was put into action against the frigate, *Wasp*, which had been sent with a garrison to enforce payment of taxes by the islanders in 1884. The ship sank off the coast, leaving only six living, and the soldiers whose bodies were recovered were buried in the Protestant graveyard.

In direct contrast to the harshness of their island environment, the people of Tory are friendly and humorous. They have a ruddy, scrubbed look—a natural result of living in a place which must be the organic equivalent of a washer-drier, constantly buffeted by waves and wind. You may well be welcomed to the island by the king of Tory himself, for the islanders have managed to hold onto the tradition of having their own king—a man who acts as a spokesperson for the island in the world of bureaucracy on the other side of the water.

Contact with the mainland is easier now than it has ever been; in West Town, the houses are festooned with satellite dishes—rusty links to the outside world during the long, dark nights of winter. However, the ferry ride can still result in green faces and unsteady legs, even in the height of summer. Visitors come to the island and swear that they will never repeat the trip, but find themselves returning again and again. One such visitor was the English artist, Derek Hill, whose hut on the northern cliffs of the island stands out starkly against a desert of grey rock. Between the clefts in the expanse of rock are crumbled smaller stones, so that the fissures look like mouths with broken teeth. It is hard to imagine a place more exposed to wind and water. Climbing here in the evening, with the wind crying and the sea beating against the rocks at the base of the cliffs, it is easy to imagine the yellow beam of the lighthouse as an all-seeing eye—closing, then opening again in a steadfast rhythm. The lighthouse is Balor's eye in reverse. This eye shines out not to destroy, but as a comfort and guide to those at the mercy of the waves of Tory.

THE BIRTH OF LUGH

A princess, as lovely as a summer's dawn over the great Atlantic, stands at a tower window, looking over the treacherous sound which separates her island from the mainland. In the distance, she can see the clear line of hills that is Ireland, no more than a few miles from her fortress on the rocks. But it might as well be a different world, for she is locked here in a tower by her father, Balor of the Evil Eye. The wind and the sea are her companions; they talk to her ceaselessly—in a whisper sometimes on the calm days of summer; in a shriek on the wild nights of winter. Her companions are kind to her, for she is easy to be kind to—her nature is sweet and her face is lovely. How strange, her ladies say, that such a mother as the witch, Ceithlinn of the Crooked Teeth, and that hideous monster, Balor of the Evil Eye, king of the Fomorians, should have produced a child as fair as Ethlinn. She is their only child. Balor was told at her birth that his fate was to be killed by his grandchild, so, from her birth, he had his daughter locked in a tower on this lonely island, far away from the eyes of men. Sometimes he comes to visit her—he knows that she draws back from him, frightened by his ugliness, frightened most of all by the great eye-lid that hangs down over the single eye in the middle of his brow. If he were to lift that eye-lid, she would die, burnt to a crisp in an instant. Yet though he sees nothing, Balor likes to think that he sees all, and he knows that his vigilance must increase now—now that his child is a young woman. Her companions are warned at pain of death to let no man onto the island, and, in particular, into the stone tower.

Opposite: *The rocky pinnacles of An Eochair Mhór on the northeast of Tory Island, County Donegal, look like giant soldiers and are known as* Saighdiúirí Bhaloir *(Balor's soldiers).*

However, it is lonely out here on the island of the towers, and the ladies long for company. So, they are happy that today two gentlewomen have

landed on the island. One is old but sharp-eyed, the other one young and muscular with ruddy cheeks. The two ladies explain how they were shipwrecked and are in need of shelter from the wind and waves. Ethlinn's companions bring them up to introduce them to their mistress, warning them, with giggles behind their hands, not to mention the word "man"—for their innocent mistress thinks that the world is made up entirely of females.

But what has the older woman taken from under her green cloak? Some kind of silver branch, it seems. She shakes it and its little bells make such a lovely sound that all the ladies fall asleep. For once, there is silence on the island; every gull, every meadowlark, wader, pipit, stonechat, every raven and peregrine and rasping corncrake—every one is silent. The swans in the lakes, the puffins on the cliffs—they all put their heads under their wing, hiding their eyes as if it was the dead of night instead of a summer afternoon. The hares sleep in their burrows; even the wind and the sea are silent—every watching eye is closed. Except the eyes of Ethlinn, who looks on in surprise as the young stranger divests herself of female clothes and starts to tell her how lovely she is—what a pearl beyond price. It is not unpleasant, however, to sit here and talk to this strange creature, and soon the sensations that she is introduced to are even more pleasurable than talking. The old woman, meanwhile, takes herself off for a walk along the cliffs, telling the young man—for so he has described himself to Ethlinn—that they must leave before the sun comes up over the eastern sea.

All evening and all night long, the couple lie in each other's arms. The young man tells the princess that his name is Cian and that he has come to the island to find the cow that Ethlinn's father stole from him. Biróg the enchantress carried him in the air over the water.

"And have you found it?" asks Ethlinn.

"Forget about the cow," he replies. "I have no more interest in it now that I have found you. Will you come with me, away from here?"

"I am afraid," says Ethlinn. "For you know my father can kill anyone he looks at with one glance of his eye."

At that moment, Biróg returns to the tower. "We must go now," she says. "The sun is rising and there is no time to waste."

"But Ethlinn will come with me, or I will not leave," protests Cian, holding the princess more tightly.

Biróg shakes her head. "I have not the strength to carry both of you in the air. You must leave her now."

Cian demurs, but Ethlinn gently pushes him towards Biróg, saying, "Go with her. If you stay here, you will die, and if I have to see you die, I will die from grief. I know that you love me, and even if I am forced to stay here for the rest of my life, watched and guarded by my father, I will have the memory of your love with me. Look to the future—all bad things will come to an end. It is for the best."

So, finally, Cian is persuaded to leave, and only just in time, for Ethlinn's companions are beginning to stretch and yawn as they awake from their long sleep, and there is the sound of thunder in the air as Balor arrives.

He sniffs. "Do I smell a man here?" he demands. The companions laugh, and Ethlinn asks innocently, "What is a man?" It is lucky that Balor does not open his eye, for his daughter's face is pink and her eyes are shining.

Nine months later, Ethlinn bears three babies. This cannot be hidden from her father, and he takes the tiny ones from her, where she lies, clutching them to her and screaming, and casts them from the sharp battlemented rocks out into the wild waves at the east of the island.

But Ethlinn, who has pulled herself to the edge of the cliffs, determined to throw herself into the waves after her children, sees what he cannot see. Before the precious bundle sinks under the water, a female figure skirts over the silver waves, and lifts one of the children above the waters, carrying it southwards towards the land of Ireland.

"What will you do now?" asks one of her maidens as she sits on the rocks and stares southwards into the eye of the noontime sun.

"I will watch the sea," Ethlinn says. "My father will still raid ships, kill sailors, demand the tribute of every third child from the people of Ireland. But I know that out of my father's dark blood will come a light for the land. As I watch the tide go in and out from my small window to this great ocean, I will know that every time it does so, the time is coming nearer when I will need to wait no more. Each tide brings me closer to the day when my child will kill the tyrant who tried to kill him, and will free the land of Ireland from his harsh servitude." She raises her voice and calls over the water, to where she can see the figure of Biróg bringing the baby safely to his foster-mother, Tailtiu.

"His name is Lugh," she calls. "He is the bright one—the gifted child. Look after him well."

Lough Neagh, Tyrone

LOCH nEACHACH

The shores of Eochaidh's Lake (from which the name Lough Neagh is derived) are tranquil, edged with farmland and small fishing craft. There is often a haze on the water so that you cannot see even to the far side of the lough. At these times, the vast stretch of water (the largest in Britain and Ireland) might almost be a sea. On days like this, is hard to imagine the lake rough and tempestuous, but it has claimed the lives of many who did not respect its moods. According to a local tradition, the lough claims one victim each year. The long shoreline is flat, lacking the dramatic beauty of Lough Leane in Killarney, and without even the small hills that encircle Lough Gur in Limerick. Like Lough Gur, this lake has great treasures of myth and story attached to it—many of them associated with how it came into being.

In one version of the story of its origin, Lough Neagh was formed when the giant Fionn got himself into a rage and tore up a huge piece of earth, throwing it towards an enemy in Scotland. The resulting vast hole became filled with water and formed the lake. Other legends claim that it marks the place where the lovers Eochaidh Mac Maireadha and Eibhliu went when they fled from her husband Mairidh, Eochaidh's father. Aonghus, the god of love and foster-father of Eibhliu, assisted the lovers by giving them a magical horse, but he told them that it must not be allowed to urinate anywhere. When the pair stopped and made their home in Ulster, however, it did so, and caused a spring to come up, which Eochaidh quickly covered. However, after a time, a woman went to the well and left the spring uncovered, so that the waters rose to drown all of the tribe, with the exception of a single girl, Lí Ban, the daughter of Eochaidh. In mythology, Eochaidh was a horse god, and the name Lough Neagh comes from the title of the descendants of Eochaidh who were the sept who lived on its banks. Other more recent folklore tells of the magical city that can be seen under the water of the lake at certain times of the day—an alternative, underwater universe, which is a mirror image of that of the living people who inhabit the banks of the lake.

Although it has been established that the area around Lough Neagh was one of the earliest inland sites of habitation in Ireland, there are relatively few ancient remains on the shores of the lake. Those antiquities that remain are for the most part from the period of Celtic Christianity rather than from earlier times. At Ardboe in Tyrone, on the southwest shore of the lough, there is one of the finest High Crosses in Ireland. Tradition has it that this Celtic church was founded by St. Colman, who mixed the mortar for the building with the milk of a magic cow. This was also a traditional site of Lughnasa celebrations, where the people of the five counties surrounding the lough met at the beginning of August. In addition to

saying the rosary in the ancient graveyard, it was traditional to wash feet, hands, face and head in the lough, as if its waters held a special power at this turning point of the year. Like many lakes in Ireland, these waters have been under threat in recent years from the levels of sewage and fertiliser run-off from the surrounding farmland, resulting in a build-up of phosphorus and nitrates and the growth of thick, choking algae on the surface of the lake. This is a threat not just to the wildlife but to the livelihood of the fishermen of the lakeside—Lough Neagh is famous in particular for its huge stocks of eels, which come here from the Sargasso Sea. Measures are being taken to counteract this pollution, and work is being done to preserve the area's environment. Such measures are welcome, for the power of this place lies in the water and the surrounding vegetation, rather than in monuments made by man. Lough Neagh is a place to visit for its natural riches—its wealth of waterfowl and plant life, and its tranquil, sheltered loveliness.

LÍ BAN THE MERMAID

A fisherman sat in his boat, far out on Lough Neagh, looking into its silver water. Muirchiú was glad that he was too far away from land for anyone to see his face, for he was weeping. His beloved had left him for a soldier, whose tales of wars and great adventures had stolen her heart and turned her head. What did it matter that Muirchiú himself was a fine, strong, young man, with black curls and ruddy cheeks, and that his father's family had fished from these shores since time before time? How could his quiet life compete with that of one who had known battle and feasting and adventures? He should have listened to his sour old uncle, Conleth, who had told him that there was no trusting women. Hadn't one of them even been responsible for the creation of the great loch itself? The lady Neagh, in her pride and arrogance, had visited the magic fountain of her people and left the cover off, and so the waters had flowed out of it until the great lake was formed, drowning all living things under its blanket of water.

There was a pull on the net and he moved swiftly to grasp it. Perhaps, he thought, he would be lucky enough to catch an eel. He tugged and tugged but whatever was caught in the net was heavier than any fish. As he pulled, determined not to lose his catch, or his new net, he began to feel worried in case it was some kind of monster—one of the great worms that live in many of the lakes of Ireland—which would pull his boat over and into the water. The thought went through his head that it would serve his sweetheart right

Above:
The waters of Lough Neagh.

if he were washed up dead on the shore. She would be sorry then. As the creature thrashed around, Muirchiú seemed to catch a glimpse of a silvery tail, the flash of fin. Finally, red in the face with exertion and panting and cursing, he managed to pull the net into the boat—and there, caught in its coil, with a look of pure fury on her face, was the most beautiful woman he had ever seen. She had silver hair, the colour of the lough water at sunset, and wide aquamarine eyes under delicate black brows. Her lips were red and the curve of her neck was as sinuous and graceful as an eel. From head to waist, she was delicately formed and bare of covering as a newborn babe, but from the waist down, she had a huge fishtail of silver and gold scales, like that of a salmon but a hundred times bigger.

"Put me down, you great oaf," said the lovely creature, thrashing her tail angrily. "Or it will be the worse for you and your children."

"And your children's children," she added as an afterthought.

The fisherman held fast but, with one final buck, the creature flipped itself out of his arms and lay on the bottom of the boat, panting nearly as heavily as Muirchiú himself.

Muirchiú finally found his voice: "What class of a creature are you?"

"I am not," said the creature in her curiously accented, archaic Gaelic, "any class of a creature, but the Princess Lí Ban, the Beauty of Women, the fairest daughter of Eochaidh Mac Maireadha and of the royal house of Ulster."

Muirchiú began to speak, but was interrupted by the woman's anxious voice.

"Oh, look—there is Dogeen. He's coming up to look for me."

At the side of the boat was an otter, swimming furiously around the stern, making whimpering noises that did indeed sound like the cries of a distressed dog. The fisherman reached over and pulled the little creature into the boat, where it jumped onto the mermaid's lap and started to lick her face furiously. She tried to pet him through the coils of the net, and then said, "Would you let me out of this tangle of threads? It's very uncomfortable sitting in them."

Muirchiú considered for a moment, eyeing her shrewdly. "Will you promise, then, not to jump out of the boat?"

Lí Ban sighed. "I promise to sit here quietly for as long as the lake is calm."

Muirchiú, like all fishermen, could tell what weather was coming by the smell of the wind and the shape of the clouds travelling across the sky. When he saw that the lake was as still as a pond and the evening sky was clear, he nodded and helped the mermaid out of the net. She settled herself down on the seat opposite him and immediately began smoothing her hair.

"So how did you end up half-fish?" asked Muirchiú, curiously.

Lí Ban grimaced. After three centuries, she was getting tired of telling the same story to every fool who caught her.

"When the fountain was opened and the waters came and drowned all my people, I was in my bower, with my little lapdog," she began briskly. "The water did not come into the bower, and I found myself face to face with the god Manannán, who told me that I was under his protection. I said that if I was doomed to live underwater, I might as well be a fish, and so I found myself a salmon, and my dog an otter, and sometimes I am fully fish and sometimes fully woman, and, then again, sometimes I have the upper shape of a woman, and I have been roaming the seas and the lake of Ireland these three hundred years. And very little of interest have I seen there, and certainly no one as handsome as you." She smiled and Muirchiú blushed furiously.

Lí Ban gave the young man a shrewd look. "I have rarely been foolish enough to be caught by a human, but I thought I heard someone weeping and was curious to see what it was about, so I came too close to your net."

Muirchiú looked sheepish. "That was me. Don't mind what I was wailing about. It was only some silly girl, but you are twice as beautiful as she is."

Lí Ban looked unimpressed. "Don't start getting any ideas, now. A daughter of a king would not be interested in a fisherman, no matter how handsome," she said sharply. "Anyway, I'm too old for you, by a few hundred years at least. But I will give you a kiss."

She leaned towards him; her lips touched his and her pale arms pulled him towards her; her long hair seemed to draw him into a net of cool softness. At first, it was like diving into deep water—he was drawn down, down into depths beyond which he had never swum. There was music down there, the deep sound of the bottom of the ocean. Then it was as if he was caught in the coils of a great eel—it was pulling him, touching him, burrowing into secret places, arousing him more and more. As his passion increased, it seemed as if the water darkened and the waves rose, and he went further and further down into the dark depths of the lake.

When he opened his eyes, he was back on land, with a crowd around him praising God that he had been saved from the water.

"What happened to you at all?" they asked. "And how did the boat manage to come back to land through such a tempest?"

"What tempest?" he asked, still fuddled.

"The one that blew up in a minute and was gone just as quickly," replied one old man, eyeing him closely. "The ones they say the mermaids call up by their singing."

But Muirchiú was not listening—realisation was dawning as he saw the empty boat, and a faint, mocking voice came into his head. Lí Ban was saying, "I only swore to stay while the water was calm, fisher-boy."

Ever after, Muirchiú would tell the story of how he had almost captured the most beautiful woman in the world. Indeed, he told the story so well that his girlfriend came back to him, begging to know if her kiss was as sweet as a mermaid's. Many years afterwards, Muirchiú heard that Lí Ban had been captured again—this time by a cleric, at Inbhar Ollarbha. The story was that a dispute had broken out between the cleric and another priest over who had the rights to the mermaid's soul. Muirchiú laughed at this, for he would not have cared about Lí Ban's soul if he could only have had her body. The word got around that the dispute had been settled by the appearance of two magical stags who had taken Lí Ban to a church where she was baptised and, in the way of the Sídh who have taken to Christianity, died immediately. But Muirchiú was not so sure of the truth of that part of the story, for he often thought, when out fishing on the lough, that he could hear the sweet, faint call of her voice, singing over the water, and even, sometimes, the echo of her clear and mocking laughter.

Ballycastle, Antrim

BAILE AN CHAISLEÁIN

Although the story of Deirdre and the Sons of Usna begins and ends at the court of King Conchobhar at Emain Macha in Armagh, perhaps its strongest connection is with the glens of Scotland, where Deirdre made her home after fleeing with her lover. The lament Deirdre sings when leaving these glens has the same emotional depth as the one she sings when her lover is killed. However, Scotland lies beyond the scope of this book, so instead we look to the extreme northeast coast of Antrim for the site of this story, to the landing place where Deirdre returned after her few short years of happiness. Tradition has it that this landing place was Ballycastle Bay, just under Fair Head. The beach at Ballycastle is a pleasant one with magnificent views towards Rathlin and Manannán's Rock. Ballycastle is a lively seaside town and the site of Lammas Fair in August, a gathering that has its roots in the Lughnasa festival. At the east end of its beach, there is a cluster of flat rocks, known as Pan's Rocks because, in the past, salt-panning was carried on here by the local people. It is said that Deirdre protested to the very end against landing here, wanting to land on Rathlin Island where at least they had the security of the sea as a barrier between themselves and the jealous Conchobhar.

Above:
"Fair Head," County Antrim, by T. Creswick.

The sea journey to Rathlin Island is well worth making, not just for the experience of a beautiful and peaceful island, and the numbers of sea birds which make the island their home, but also for the friendliness and kindness of the people who live there—there is nothing quite like the feeling of staying on such an island when the last of the day visitors have left and the island sinks into its world of quietness. Folk tradition says that Rathlin was formed when Fionn's huge mother tripped and dropped a pile of stones in the bay, on her way to Scotland to buy whiskey—she lies drowned under the water, and, in stormy weather, people say, "The old witch is kickin." The idea of the *Cailleach* or Old Witch as creator of the landscape links this northeastern point of Ireland with that extreme southwestern one—Béara.

Not far from Ballycastle is Torr Head. It was there that the traitorous warrior Barach forced Fergus Mac Róich—who had taken on the safety of Deirdre and the Sons of Usna as his personal responsibility—to leave his charges and dine with him at his fort. The journey around the coast from Ballycastle to Torr Head passes by Fair Head, where there are signposted walks on the cliffs. The small valley of Lough na Cranagh holds a *crannóg* in a lake hedged by green hills. Here, the trees and the gentle hills give relief from the sometimes overpowering drama and tempest of the coastal views. Fair Head is also the site where yet another giant has his residence—not, in this case, a figure from mythology, but a character from local folklore, known as the Grey Man. This cloaked figure may be seen striding along the cliffs, looking out towards the sea when a storm is brewing. Perhaps this figure is connected with the grey-cloaked god, Manannán, for the rock that bears his name is not far out to sea, in the wild Sea of Moyle where the Children of Lir spent the most miserable part of their time in exile. Here you feel closer to the Mull of Kintyre than to Ireland; and indeed, at those times in the past when land travel was made difficult by bogs and great forests, Scotland would have been more easily accessible than many parts of Ireland. It is on Fair Head that during the reign of Elizabeth I, the old Gaelic chieftain, Sorley Boy, screamed his madness and grief when he heard the shrieks coming across the sound from Rathlin. He had sent the women and children of his clan there for safety but an invading fleet, led by Drake and Norris, landed on the island and butchered every one of them.

This is country that can best be appreciated by those prepared to do some walking, to immerse themselves in hidden valleys and wild headlands. Not far away is Cushendall and the site of Oisín's Grave—a Neolithic court grave on Tievebullagh mountain. This is the country of Fionn and the Fianna, of hunters racing with their hounds and their horns down narrow glens towards the sea. If Deirdre's ghost wanders here, it is a lonely one, continually looking eastwards across the sea towards the glens of Scotland.

THE TRAGEDY OF DEIRDRE

I was there at her birth, and I was there at her death. And if I had known what I know now, at the time of her birth—if I had known of the sorry destruction that her lovely face would bring on us all—I might have taken that little crying baby and held her tight against me, and stopped her crying by stopping her breath at my breast. And I would have done it for love of that little one, and for the honour of our king and the safety of our world.

She was born to sorrow—in the middle of the feasting, when her mother was crying out in pain in the birthing-room, the prophecy made by Cathbad was that this child's beauty would be such that it would bring great sorrow to the land of Ireland. So there were many would have agreed with me if I had taken her and killed her gently then; but the king laughed, and said no, for he was one who always wanted the best of everything and why should he not have the most beautiful woman in the world as his bride? So he sent Deirdre away into hiding, with no companion but me—Leabharcham, an old woman poet—to look after her in her house in the forest. There she grew more beautiful every day, and more gracious, but always a little serious for want of the companionship of others of her age. And while her hair grew blacker and her eyes bluer, the king, Conchobhar, grew greyer and grosser in his palace at Emain Macha, and it tore my heart to think of his lewdness in taking my sweet nursling to his bed.

He would come and visit her and sit her on his knee and try to make her laugh, but she looked at him with big, solemn eyes and not a smile on her lips. And I could see that the time was approaching when her beauty would be such that Conchobhar would wait no longer. So I cannot tell whether it was more by design than by chance that my tongue slipped one day, when Deirdre, watching the snow fall from the window of our lonely fortress, said, "Look, Leabharcham—there is a raven feeding on a dead calf in the snow. I would wish that I should meet a man with such black hair, such red lips, and such white skin."

And I, busy with my spinning, and my mind on my work, said, "In truth, Conchobhar is not such a one—though I knew him when he was a handsome

Below:
Pan's Rocks on the Antrim coast.

enough lad, before age and greed made him as he is. But such a one is Naoise, the eldest of the sons of Usna—he indeed has that beauty."

And Deirdre gave me no peace until I had arranged for her to see Naoise. Then she teased him and tormented him until he began to come secretly to our hiding place. I needed no powers of foreseeing to know what would happen next. Indeed, I was a little careless with my locking and barring; and, one morning, I awoke to find my ward gone and a ring left on my pillow, with a message of love from my girl. No doubt, I would have suffered a hard punishment from Conchobhar after that, were it not for the fact that I am a satirist and he knew that my tongue could bring him out in a rash of boils that would keep him off his throne for a month.

During the next few years, I heard about Deirdre only from hearsay; for she and Naoise and his two brothers, who loved him so much that they would not leave him, wandered far and wide—to Ballyshannon in the west, to Howth in the east—always moving on for fear that Conchobhar would find them. I heard that they went to Scotland, where they found some peace at last. But then a local king fell in love with Deirdre and tried to kill Naoise in order to have her for himself. So Deirdre and the sons of Usna fled into the wild mountains, and my dear girl told me afterwards that that was the happiest period she knew in all her life, though times were hard and they were often cold and hungry, and she buried a little baby girl on the side of a blue hill.

That is why, I think, she wept so hard when Conchobhar sent messengers to tell the sons of Usna that they were pardoned and that they could return to Emain Macha and be received by him. I think that she saw more than Naoise did, for I had trained her in seeing within and seeing ahead, and she was not blinded by the warrior's code of honour and loyalty in the way her husband was. For although Conchobhar pretended forgiveness, his memory of Deirdre was like a wound gone septic with time, rather than one that has healed in any clean way. He planned the betrayal of the Usna, forcing the good warrior, Fergus Mac Róich, who had gone to Scotland acting as guarantor for the king's good intentions, to abandon them when they landed on the Antrim coast. As soon as they touched land, the treacherous Barach, acting under the king's instructions, invited Fergus to a feast. As the warrior was under *geis* never to refuse such an invitation, he was forced to go with Barach. Deirdre and the Sons of Usna continued the journey to Emain Macha without him.

Deirdre told me afterwards that she knew all along that Conchobhar meant evil, and that, every step of the way, she begged Naoise and his brothers to go no nearer to his court. Perhaps Naoise might have listened to her, but I think that the brothers felt they had listened too long to this woman who had brought them into exile; and they insisted that it was against their honour to turn back now that they had made the decision to return to the kingdom of Conchobhar.

So they came to Emain Macha, and Conchobhar did not ask them to eat and drink with him, but sent them to the house of the Red Branch, so that Deirdre was sure then he meant to kill them. Conchobhar sat and drank and laughed with his nobles at Emain Macha, knowing that his quarry was safe nearby. Suddenly, he called out, "Is there anyone who will go to the House of the Red Branch and tell me if Deirdre still has her beauty, her black hair, her blue eye?"

As quick as a flash, I was there before him, volunteering. He did not look best pleased to see me, but, despite my years, I can still move quickly, and I took off before he could change his mind, and came to the house where Deirdre and Naoise were playing chess. She was as lovely as she had ever been—lovelier even, for love and grief and long suffering had given her the dignity of a queen. We embraced and cried, and I warned them of Conchobhar's treachery and told them to bar the doors against any other comers. Then I returned to Conchobhar and told him: "In truth, your majesty, Deirdre has suffered from her hard life—her black hair is grey, her white skin wrinkled and yellow; her teeth are brown and crooked; and her eyes have faded to the colour of rain. She is no loss as a wife."

At first, he seemed satisfied with this, and ordered more wine, but then I could see his brain working. In truth, though he acted evilly towards my beloved girl, I have to admit that he was not a stupid man. He called out again: "Is there anyone who will go to the House of the Red Branch and tell me if Deirdre still holds her beauty, her black hair, her blue eye?"

And that little creeping thing, Tordre, jumped up and said that he would go, and I followed as fast as my old legs could carry me. But I was too late, because, although the doors were barred, the creature climbed high and looked in through the window over the door, and saw the two lovers there. I heard Deirdre's cry, for she must have looked up and seen him, and Naoise threw a spear which blinded Tordre in one eye—but he ran away so quickly that I could not catch him, though I cursed him and all his family for generations to come.

The rest is known to all—how Conchobhar sent a great army to re-capture Deirdre, and the sons of Usna were killed by their former companions, the three of them standing in a circle around her, protecting her with their shields. Deirdre, to her great sorrow, did not die on that day. She spent a year with Conchobhar, being used by him as a bull uses a cow, and never once did I see a smile cross her lips. It is true that at the beginning he tried to cajole her, to tempt her with presents and sweet words; but her look was the same to him whether he beat her or begged her—she had nothing to give him but dull and stubborn hatred. At the end of the year, he asked her, "Who is it that you hate most in the world, my Queen of Sorrows?"

She shrugged and answered him: "Apart from yourself, King of Shame, it would be Eoghan Mac Durthacht, for it was he who struck the blow that killed my beloved."

So Conchobhar told her that she would spend the next year with Eoghan, and perhaps after that she would be sent to another warrior who had helped to kill the sons of Usna. He took her in his chariot with Eoghan, and brought me along to punish me by seeing her pain, and they travelled the great road from Emain Macha. It was a snowy day. The sky was bright blue and only the black shapes of the forest broke the whiteness of the hills. Deirdre had scratched her face with her nails, trying to ruin her beauty, and she stood slumped in the chariot like an old woman, but Conchobhar, having brought her to this, still could not leave matters alone. He said, "That face you have on you, woman, between me and Eoghan, is like the look of a ewe when she is caught between two rams."

He and Eoghan both laughed loudly. Deirdre said nothing. I saw what she was going to do, but I did nothing to stop her, for I thought that in death her spirit might find its way to the blue hillside in Scotland and to her beloved Naoise. She flung herself from the chariot against a great rock that was beside the road there. Conchobhar's laugh was stopped in his throat and he stood silent, looking down at her body in the snow, where the red blood flowed over white skin and black hair.

Giant's Causeway, Antrim

CLOCHÁN NA BHFOMHARAIGH

Established as a UNESCO World site in 1986, the Giant's Causeway and the area around it on the north Antrim coast has long been a favourite site for tourists to Ireland. It was "discovered" by polite society at the end of the seventeenth century and was not marked on maps until 1714, despite the fact that some of the earliest settlers in Ireland are likely to have lived on the north Antrim coastline, as the flint-factories on Rathlin Island testify. From the time of its discovery, the causeway became increasingly popular, so that by Victorian times, any traveller to Ireland considered it a compulsory stop along their route. Visitors such as William Thackeray and the Halls gave detailed descriptions of it. Some of the travellers, having seen the somewhat exaggerated prints of the wonders of the causeway, may have been a little underwhelmed. While the black basalt rocks, which

Above:
W.H. Bartlett's engraving,
"Scene at the Giant's Causeway,"
County Antrim.

make up the causeway, are interesting in a geological sense, the area they cover is not a huge one. Nevertheless, there are estimated to be 40,000 of these rocks, and they are set in stunningly beautiful surroundings of magnificent cliffs which have formed their own strange shapes and columns.

Tourism, with the guides, postcards, boat-trips and hawking, while providing an income for local people, also brought its own dangers of overcrowding and, before safeguards were put into place, in some cases involved the actual removal of rocks from the causeway. Now, access to the causeway and cliffs is better controlled and, while there are still crowds in summer, a visit during spring or autumn, preferably in the early morning, can be made with nothing but dozens of sea birds for company. At any time of the year (with the possible exception of wild winter days, when the cold wind can cut through any number of layers of clothing), the cliff walk is well worth making, with magnificent views to the west to Donegal and eastwards towards the blue outline of the Scottish coast.

The causeway (*Clochán na bhFomharaigh*—"the stepping stones of the Fomorians"), once believed to be the work of giants, is in fact a totally natural formation. Sixty million years ago, lava flowed towards the sea, cooling to become black basalt and, in the meantime, cracking to form the honeycomb of shaped rocks—in a similar way to the way in which mud cracks when it dries. Many layers of lava flows resulted in the variety of shapes and sizes, from the tall columns and the misshapen cliffs to the flatter causeway itself. While Thackeray described the causeway as "a remnant of chaos," in some ways it is the very opposite—an example of a natural wonder that seems so regular and ordered as to have to be man-made, the work of some demented and obsessive giant. And so the stories go. According to local stories, the giant Fionn Mac Cumhaill, transformed by folklore into a comic figure rather than the great and jealous warrior he comes across as in the legends, built the causeway as a route to fight a giant in Scotland. When he reached Scotland and saw his enemy, he realised that he was bigger than he thought, and ran back towards Ireland, tearing the causeway up behind him. The remnants on the Scottish side lie around Fingal's Cave on the island of Staffa, and take the form of basalt columns. There are many stories about Fionn still remembered by the people of Antrim—his cleverness, his strength, and, in cases, his bad temper, as when he turned his mother into rock because she was nagging him for going too slowly as he was building the causeway.

However, there are also other, less light-hearted stories associated with this wild stretch of coast—of shipwrecks and deaths at sea, and the hard life of these hardy people. One of the great waves of Ireland, the wave of Tuaidhe was said to come in at Ballintoy, to the east of the causeway, and Ballycastle Harbour is notorious for its treacherous currents. If you make the walk along the cliffs eastwards towards Port Moon, you will pass Port na Spánaigh, where the Spanish Armada ship, the *Girona*, foundered in 1588. There were 1,300 people drowned in the wreck. The remains of the ship were discovered in 1967, when the gold and jewels found by divers were transferred to the Ulster Museum. The coastline is deeply indented and the little harbours are a litany of musical names—Port Coon, Port Moon, Portnaboe. The final point on the cliff walk, Dunseverick Castle, stands on the ancient site of Dún Sobhairce, one of the four royal roads which led from Tara. It was at Dún Sobhairce that King Rónán slew his son in jealousy and began the slaughter that would see the death of his friends and family. It is a fitting point to stop and reflect on an area that has changed so little since the first flows of lava headed northwards, and the fiery stone met icy water to become a landscape set apart.

FIONN'S VISITOR

Opposite: *The distinctive stones of the Causeway.*

Fionn often went to fight the giants in Scotland, and he made the Giant's Causeway as a convenient way of getting across without wetting his feet. However, there was a Scottish giant once, who decided to come across the causeway and fight with Fionn. Fionn's wife spotted him as the huge creature made his way over across the stones, and realised that he was twice the size of her husband. When he reached Fionn's house, the giant knocked on the door.

Bang, bang, bang.

Fionn's wife opened the door (we are not told which wife it was, but it seems likely that it could have been Gráinne, as she was obviously a woman of quick wits).

"Good day to you," said the giant. "I'm here to fight your husband."

"Are you indeed?" asked Fionn's wife. "Well, fair play to you. You had better come in and rest yourself, for he's away hunting. He'll be back soon."

The giant came in and sat crouched by the fire, and the woman of the house offered him a drink and began to sing softly to the figure sleeping in the settle bed.

The giant took a closer look into the bed. There was a huge warrior there, with a bearded face and shoulders like an ox.

"Who is that?" He asked the woman of the house.

"That's the new baby," said the woman. "The ba—the last of fifteen. The rest are out hunting with their daddy. Isn't he a fine lad?"

The giant nodded and came forward to have a closer look. "Indeed he is."

The figure gave a little moan.

"Ah, the poor baba. Sure, isn't he teething?" said the woman. "Would you mind putting some salve on his gums while I heat some milk for him?" She handed the giant a pot of white ointment.

The giant cautiously put his ointment-covered finger into the creature's mouth, then yelped and jumped away.

"He's after taking a big bite out of me," he said. "Didn't you say he was only getting his teeth?"

The woman sounded surprised.

"You must have hurt his poor gums. Well, he is teething. It's his wisdom teeth he's getting. Sure every baby of Fionn's is born with a full set of teeth apart from those last four."

"And a big hairy face?" asked the giant. "And legs like tree-trunks?"

The woman smiled indulgently.

"Indeed, that's the case. I'm telling you, I had a terrible time when this lad was born. Would you like me to tell you all about it? Three weeks in labour I was...but of course it was worth it—isn't he a grand little fella? But not one of them is a pick on their father."

The giant took off out the door and ran all the way to Scotland, pulling the causeway up behind him as he went.

Fionn's wife laughed and said to the figure on the bed, who could no longer keep the grin off his face: "Well, husband dear, you can get up now. I don't think that fella will be coming over looking to fight with you again."

Emain Macha, Armagh

Emain Macha (the name means "the twins of Macha") or Navan Fort, as it is also known, lies close to the town of Armagh in a countryside of rounded hills and hidden valleys, the south Armagh borderland. The great bowl-shaped mound is sited on a hill, surrounded by a circular rampart and ditch and with commanding views over the countryside. This is the place that was the main home of the Red Branch warriors, the army of Conchobhar Mac Neasa. Conchobhar was the king who was said to rule Ulster during the period when the great epic, the *Táin*, was set. He was the arch-enemy of Maeve and the sovereign lord of the great hero, Cú Chulainn. Emain Macha is an impressive structure and has a long history. The main remaining structure dates from around 100BC but the original settlement date was earlier, possibly as early as 700BC. It is one of the great royal sites of the pagan Celtic Iron Age—an honour shared with Tara, Cruachain and Dún Ailinne. Excavations on the mound began in 1963, and involved carefully removing the earthen mound and examining what lay beneath.

There seem to have been various phases of activity on the site. It was established that the inner structure was rebuilt nine times and the outer stockade six times during the period 700–100BC. It appears that, originally, five rings of huge oak posts were set up, which were then filled with thousands of limestone boulders to form a cairn 2.8 metres (9 feet) high. Then, the timber building was deliberately burnt and the remaining structure was covered with turf. This indicates that there was a ritual element in the construction, the meaning of which has been lost to us. The evidence seems to point to strong connections with the cult of sovereignty of the priest kings of the Iron Age who had sacred, as well as secular, duties. There are no historical sources on the founding of Emain Macha although it was certainly a palace, according to the descriptions in the stories. It is said that Conchobhar had three households at Emain Macha—the *Craobh Ruadh*, or Red Branch; the *Téte Brec*, or Place of the Shining Hoard, where the king kept his weapons and treasure; and the *Craobh Dearg* or Ruddy Branch, where he kept the severed heads of his enemies.

Above: *A view of Armagh by H. McManus.*

Emain Macha, as ritual centre as well as the home of the king, was a centre for the *aonach*, the seasonal meeting where buying and selling went on, games and horse races and feasts were held, and rituals were celebrated by the tribe.

There are actually two mounds on the site, both of which have been excavated. By the late Iron Age, the centre of one of these mounds seems to have held a huge central pole—perhaps of oak. The word "branch" in the associated place names and the fact that nearby in Armagh there was a sacred oak grove seems to indicate that trees played an important role in the ritual here; the oak was sacred to the great god, the Daghdha. However, the place was undoubtedly also linked with Macha, the goddess of sovereignty, associated most particularly with war and horses—the epitome of a warrior-caste deity. Cú Chulainn's horse was called the Grey of Macha; this was the horse who wept tears of blood when his master died.

Macha is an ambiguous figure, appearing in different tales under different guises. Her name signifies "pasture," indicating a strong connection with the land and with fertility. In one account, she is recorded as being "of the Red Tresses" and the daughter of Aed Ruadh, a pre-Christian king of Ireland. The redness, associated with gold, with glory and power, but also with blood, is reflected in the warriors of the Red Branch, and the redness of Conchobhar's three houses. When Macha appeared to Cú Chulainn, she had red eyebrows, red hair and a red cloak. When her father died and she claimed sovereignty, her claim was disputed by her cousins and she did battle for the kingship. The story of her victory over her enemies includes an account of her sleeping with each of them in the guise of a leper—no doubt, an echo of the ancient ritual where the king was seen as mated with the land. Macha was the victor and, in this particular account of the founding of Emain Macha, she brought her enemies in chains to build the great mound. She is said to have traced the outline of the fort with her brooch.

The hill has fine views of old farms and fertile pastures with peacefully grazing cattle. Five kilometres away, the twin towers of one of Armagh's two cathedrals can be seen. The importance of the area continued into Christian times. St. Patrick is said to have founded a church on what is now called Cathedral Hill and it became an important centre of Christianity in Ireland—Ard Macha. Armagh became a famous centre of learning and the victim of centuries of Viking attacks because of the wealth of its monastery.

The drumlin hills give a feeling of entering a hidden country, and the Emain Macha complex itself gives the visitor a feeling of moving into a ritual enclosure, as you walk the circular route through banks covered in with bluebells and primroses, where gnarled trees shelter nests of singing birds. There are two mounds, two cathedrals, and two towers—all these doubles echo the twins of Macha and reflect her ambiguous nature. The gentle, folded hills of South Armagh have witnessed Macha in her guise of bloody goddess as well as that of fertile mother. In the distant past, the hilly, boggy Fews acted as a barrier to invasion from the Pale, and, during the years of trouble in Northern Ireland, the twisting roads of south Armagh saw more than their share of violent death. However, on a fine day in April, it is possible to see only Macha's other face—the smiling face of the goddess of rich pastures and green life.

MACHA'S CURSE

Crunnchu of Ulster had always been a silent man, small and dark and of quiet ways; but nonetheless, women liked him. After his wife died, though, he became more silent and sombre and spent his time either out on the hills with his cows or in his house alone, watching the fire and often drinking heavily. On one such day, as he sat there on his own, a woman entered the house—a tall, finely built woman with hair the colour of polished copper, and green eyes. She looked down to where Crunnchu was stretched on the couch but said nothing, only seated herself at the hearth and stirred the flames. Crunnchu too said nothing, unsure as to whether he was half-asleep and dreaming this beauty before him. But later, when the woman began to prepare food for the evening meal and went outside to milk the cows, he knew that it was no dream. He went outside after her. The mist was gathering over the low hills around his farm, and the cows rubbed up against her as if they knew her. He said, "Woman, who are you, and why have you come to me?"

She smiled. "There is no need for you to learn my name," she said. "Call me one of your own liking. But I have watched you and know that you are a man of silent ways and a steady heart, and in truth also I like your looks. So I have come to be with you."

Crunnchu did not know quite what to make of this, but that evening, when he lay in his bed by the fireside, the woman came to him and laid a hand on his thigh, and, from that day, they were together.

Nine months passed, and with the woman's hard work and canny ways, and the seemingly miraculous bounty of his land, Crunnchu became richer than ever. He marvelled at his wife's strength—how she could run like the wind halfway up the mountain after a straying horse or heifer, her hair streaming behind her. How she could lift tubs of butter and pull a ploughshare as cleanly as an ox; how she never tired, whether in dairy or stable or field, or in his bed at night. He wondered sometimes if she was of the Sídh, but never dared to ask her, though sometimes his ignorance gnawed at his heart, especially when he thought of the child she was carrying in her womb.

Then, one day when the winter snows had melted from the hills and the scent of the first primroses was in the air, strangers came travelling through his *dún*, telling of a great gathering to be held, with horse races and tournaments and feasting. Crunnchu, proud of his success, decided that he would like to see something of the world beyond his farm and asked his wife to come with him to the gathering.

"For I'm sure," he said, "that I will have the finest lady of anyone there."

His wife grimaced and shook her head; she was never comfortable with his compliments, which was just as well, as he gave them rarely.

"No," she said. "I will not go with you, for I am near my time, and I would ask you to stay with me. We do not need such entertainment."

"But I wish to go," said Crunnchu, hurt by her tone. "Can I not show you off?"

"Neither show me off nor speak about me at the fair," said the woman. "Or it will be the worse for both of us."

Crunnchu went off a little sulkily, but soon recovered when he reached the great assembly, with its stalls and races and heroes showing off their feats of arms. He watched the races with eagerness and drank more deeply than he had for many months. At the ninth hour, the king's chariot came forward, and his horses—a pair of twinned greys—won every race. Crunnchu's companion, seeing them pass the post for the fifth time, said, "Indeed, there is nothing faster in Ireland than those horses."

However, Crunnchu, fuddled with drink, said proudly, "Indeed, my wife could run faster then those two!"

It chanced that the king overheard his shout, and had Crunnchu brought before him.

"So what is this about your wife running faster then my best beasts? Do you mean to mock me?"

Crunnchu, feeling considerably more sober now that he had been manhandled and dragged before the king, shook his head and said, "Indeed, I meant nothing by it."

But the king looked angrier than ever and said, "What false boast was this, then? Are you a liar to be flogged before the people?"

Stung by the king's words, Crunnchu replied, "Indeed, I do not lie—for it is the truth. My wife could outrun your horses if she were here today."

The king laughed. "Then, let her be brought here, and if she cannot do so, you will be put to death."

When the messengers went to Crunnchu's farm, at first the woman refused to come with them, begging to be left alone to have her child, for her time was very near. But finally, when they told her that Crunnchu would be put to death if she did not come, she agreed to go to the king. They travelled

to where the assembly was, and the red-haired woman turned to her husband and said, "You have been unwise, my husband. It is not right that I should be stared at by this crowd, and I so near my time. What is it that the king wants?"

The king himself replied. "Your husband has boasted that you can outrun my two best horses. We have set up a racecourse for you to do this."

The woman went pale.

"Do not ask me to do this, noble king, for the children in my womb will come very soon. I beg your mercy—wait until after I have given birth and then I will run for you. Do not shame me in my hour of weakness."

The king refused.

The woman looked at Crunnchu. "Can you not save me from this, husband?" she asked.

But he only hung his head.

Then she looked around the great crowd of men. "Someone among you plead for me," she said. "For has not a mother borne each of you?"

However, there was no mercy on any of the faces looking at her—only greedy anticipation of wagers laid and the thrill of the race. Perhaps in some there was even a desire to see the woman shamed and humiliated; but most of the men there, if they were thinking at all, thought only of possible loss or gain. Finally, the woman shouted, "Shame on you all then, and shame on your children."

The king said, "Enough of this—start the race." Then he asked, "Woman, what is your name?"

The woman replied, "My name is Macha and well you shall all remember it."

The race began, and some turned their eyes away when they saw the woman, who seemed hardly able to stand, pull herself to the starting post. She took off her heavy robe and let down her long red hair, standing in her shift, her belly out before her like a plum ready to burst. At first, it seemed as if she could have no chance against the chariot drawn by the two swift horses, for she staggered forward for the first few yards. But as the race went on, something seemed to take her over, as if her anger had given her a strength beyond the lot of humans. By the halfway mark, she was running like the wind, and those who had betted on the king's greys were beginning to look downcast.

As she raced past the finish post, far ahead of the two sweating horses, the sky darkened and Macha gave a great cry and fell to the ground. There on the

Opposite:
Emain Macha, County Armagh.

race track, before anyone could come to succour or shield her, she gave birth to two children—a boy and a girl.

All the men who heard the cry she gave were seized with a weakness, so that each one felt he had no more strength than that of a woman in childbirth. Macha drew herself up from the ground and stood before them. And now all that were there knew that she was no farmer's wife, but a goddess. She said to them, "I have won the race, men of Ulster; and know that as punishment for your greed and your cruelty to a woman in pain, I put on you this curse. In your time of greatest need, the men of Ulster will be laid on their backs with a sickness which will have them crying in agony, weakened, at the mercy of their enemies. You will be like women at the time of their travail; you will know agony and helplessness; and there will be no one to help you. This sickness will remain on you for five days and four nights and it will continue to sicken your children until the ninth generation. And, as this is the place where my shame was seen, it will be called forever Emain Macha, or the place of the twins of Macha."

"And as for you," she said, turning to give her husband one last cold glance. "You could have known riches and happiness such as no man has ever been granted. But instead you will live in sorrow and want, and misfortune brought on by your boasting tongue."

Then she gathered up her children and walked away from the red blood that spattered the green grass and from the men who lay groaning in their seats, unable to move, powerless as new-born infants against the curse of Macha.

Time Chart

<table>
<tr><th>PERIOD</th><th>DATES IN IRELAND</th><th>ASSOCIATED FEATURES</th><th>ASSOCIATED SITES CONNECTED TO STORIES IN THIS BOOK</th><th>CORRESPONDS IN LEGENDARY TIME TO:</th><th>WORLD HISTORY CONTEXT</th></tr>
<tr><td>Palaeolithic Era</td><td>Pre-7500BC</td><td>None.

No evidence of human habitation in Ireland.</td><td>None.</td><td rowspan="4">The Mythological Cycle: stories of the Tuatha Dé Danann and the invasions of Ireland.</td><td>Traces of pottery from Japan, Brazil, the Sudan. Cave paintings in northern Spain and southern France.</td></tr>
<tr><td>Mesolithic Era (normally starts 12000BC but the second Ice Age in Ireland prevented habitation before 8000BC)</td><td>c.7500BC –3500BC</td><td>Middens, flint, shell and food remains. Earliest stone structures.</td><td>Possibly Carrowmore, Sligo.</td><td>Evidence of Neolithic culture/early farming in Near East, moving west and north.</td></tr>
<tr><td>Neolithic Era</td><td>c.3500BC –2000BC</td><td>Megalithic tombs: portal, passage, court and wedge tombs.</td><td>Carrowkeel, Newgrange, Knowth and Dowth, Mound of the Hostages at Tara, cairn on Knockainey, remains at Uisneach.</td><td>First pyramids in Egypt.
Emergence of Minoan civilisation in Crete.</td></tr>
<tr><td>Bronze Age</td><td>c.2000BC –300BC</td><td>Standing stones, stone circles, beginnings of hill-forts.</td><td>Barrows at Knockainey, stone circles on Béara. Dún Aonghusa, as a hill-fort on a promontory, is thought to have been in its heyday during the Bronze Age.</td><td>Classical Greece.</td></tr>
<tr><td>Celtic Iron Age</td><td>c.300BC –500AD</td><td>Promontory forts, ringforts, hill-forts, cashels and cathairs.</td><td>The great ritual sites such as Emain Macha, Tara and Cruachain.
Promontory forts at Howth, Caherconree, Béara, Dún Aonghusa and Tory.
Grianán of Aileach.</td><td>Ulster Cycle
Fianna Cycle
(Early centuries AD).</td><td>Rise and fall of the Roman Empire, Great Wall of China.</td></tr>
<tr><td>Early Christian Era</td><td>c.500AD– first Viking invasions</td><td>Small churches, beehive huts, ogham stones. Ringforts still in use.</td><td>Ecclesiastical sites all over Ireland including those mentioned in stories at Inis Glora, Ardagh, St. Mullins.</td><td>Cycles of the Kings.</td><td>"Dark Ages" in Europe.</td></tr>
</table>

Glossary of Main Characters

AENGUS
Last king of the Fir Bolg; in legend, the builder of Dún Aonghusa on Inishmore. Not connected with Aonghus of the Tuatha Dé Danann.

AIDEEN
A form of Étaín.

AIFE, DAUGHTER OF DEALBHEATH
Princess, changed by malice into a crane and accidentally killed by Manannán Mac Lir.

AILBE
Daughter of Cormac Mac Airt.

AILBHE
Sister of Aobh and Aoife.

AILEACH
Scottish princess and wife of Friguan; the Grianán of Aileach was said to be built in her name.

AILILL ANGHUBHA
Brother of Eochaidh Aireamh, the high king who was the husband of Étaín.

AILILL MAC MÁTA
King of Connacht; husband of Maeve.

AILILL ÓLOM
King of Munster; rapist of Áine.

ÁINE
Goddess of the sun, brightness, fertility; tutelary goddess of Knockainey.

AOBH
Mother of the Children of Lir.

AODH
One of the children of Lir; changed into a swan by Aoife.

AOIBHEALL
Woman of the Sídh, associated with County Clare.

AOIFE
Daughter of Bodhbh; enchantress; second wife of Lir and stepmother to his children.

AONGHUS ÓG
One of the Tuatha Dé Danann, God of youth and love; Lord of Brú na Bóinne.

ART
High king; son of Conn; husband of Dealbhchaem.

BADBH
War-goddess; one of the three battle furies—often appeared as a crow.

BALOR NA SÚILE NIMHE (OF THE POISON EYE)
God of the Fir Bolg; killed by his grandson Lugh at the Second Battle of Moytura.

BANBA
One of the three sister goddesses of sovereignty of Ireland.

BARACH
Red Branch warrior; betrayer of the Sons of Usna.

BÉCUMA
Woman of the Sídh, sent into exile to Ireland; wife of Conn of the Hundred Battles.

BIRÓG
Woman of the Sídh who rescued Lugh from his grandfather.

BLÁI DEARG
See Sadhbh.

BLÁTHNAID
Daughter of Iuchar; wife of Cú Roí; lover of Cú Chulainn.

BÓCHNA
Mother of the seer Fintan; one of the first women to come to Ireland.

BODHBH DEARG
Tutelary god of Slievenamon; father of Aoife.

BÓINN
Goddess of the Boyne and of cattle; mother of Aonghus by the Daghdha.

BOLG
Deity associated with lightning; the Fir Bolg are his people. There are other interpretations of the word *Bolg*.

BRAN
Hound of Fionn; child of his sister when she took the form of a hound.

BRES
Half-Fomorian, half of the race of the Tuatha Dé Danann, Bres was elected their king after Nuadhu lost his arm but soon became a tyrant. He was eventually defeated by the troops of the Tuatha Dé Danann at the Second Battle of Moytura.

BRICRIU
Warrior, known as "Poisoned Tongue," he caused dissension wherever he went.

BRIGHID, BRIGID
Goddess of smithwork, poetry and healing; later, the saint born in Louth and founder of the monastery at Kildare; celebrated at Imbolc on February 1, the beginning of spring.

BUAN
One of the first people to come to Ireland, companion of Cessair.

CAER IOBHARMHÉITH
Woman of the Sídh; wife of Aonghus.

CAILLEACH BHÉARRA
See Hag of Béara.

CAIRBRE LIFEACHAIR
King of Ireland, son of Cormac Mac Airt.

CAIRNEACH
Saint who cursed Muircheartach Mac Erca.

CAMÓG
One of the three Hags of Keshcorann.

CAOILTE MAC RÓNÁIN
One of the Fianna—its greatest runner .

CATHBAD
Druid and seer of the court of King Conchobhar Mac Nessa.

CEAT MAC MAGHACH
Renowned Connacht warrior sent by King Cairbre against the Fir Bolg.

CEITHLINN OF THE CROOKED TEETH
Wife of Balor and mother of Ethlinn.

CERNET
Mistress of Cormac Mac Airt.

CESSAIR
The first person to land in Ireland—she and all her people, except for Fintan, were killed in a great flood.

CIAN
Lover of Ethlinn, father of Lugh.

CLIACH
Famous harper who fell in love with one of the daughters of Bodhbh.

CLÍODHNA
Woman of the Sídh, lover of Aonghus Óg, associated with west Cork.

CNÚ DEARÓIL
Fionn's musician.

COLMAN
Seventh-century monk and saint.

COLMCILLE
Sixth-century Donegal saint and monk; founder of the great monastery at Iona.

CONAIRE MÓR
High King of Ireland; son of Mes Buachalla and a bird-spirit; grandson of Étaín.

CÓNAL
One the three great champions of the Red Branch warriors.

CONALL CEARNACH
Warrior sent by King Cairbre against the Fir Bolg.

CONALL, SON OF AENGUS
Son of the last king of the Fir Bolg, killed by Cú Chulainn.

CONÁN
Warrior of the Fianna and brother of Goll Mac Morna.

CONCHOBHAR MAC NEASA
King of Ulster during the period of the *Táin* and the Red Branch; killer of the Sons of Usna.

CONN
One of the Children of Lir, changed into a swan by Aoife.

CONN OF THE HUNDRED BATTLES
Conn Cét Chathach; high king; husband of Bécuma.

CONNLA
Son of Conn of the Thousand Battles, Connla was enticed away to the Land of Youth by a woman of the Sídh.

CORANN
Harper and poet of Tuatha Dé Danann.

CORMAC MAC AIRT
High king of Ireland; great law-giver; travelled to the realm of Manannán at Bealtaine, or May Eve.

COS CORACH
Musician associated with Slievenamon.

CRAOBH RUA
Red Branch warriors—soldiers of Conchobhar Mac Neasa, they were based at Emhain Macha.

CREDE
Woman of the Sídh and lover of Art, son of Conn.

CRIMTHAN
King who reputedly reigned for only one year (74AD) and is said to be buried on Howth Head.

CROMDES
A druid and magician of the Tuatha Dé Danann.

CRUNNCHU
Husband of Macha.

CÚ CHULAINN
Great hero of Ulster and of the Red Branch.

CÚ ROÍ
Great magician; killed by Cú Chulainn.

CUILLEANN
One of the three Hags of Keshcorann.

DA DEARGA
Host of the house in the Wicklow mountains where Conaire met his death.

DAGHDHA
The Great God; mated with Bóinn and the Morrigan; builder of Aileach; Keeper of the Cauldron of Plenty.

DÁIRE
Farmer of Cooley; owner of the Donn of Cooley.

DANU
Great goddess; mother of the Tuatha Dé Danann.

DEALBHCHAEM
Princess, rescued and married to Art.

DEALBHEATH
Legendary king who was the son of Ogma.

DEIRDRE
Lover of Naoise.

DIAN CÉCHT
Healer of the Tuatha Dé Danann who restored the wounded at the battle of Moytura.

DIARMUID UA DHUIBHNE
One of the Fianna; lover of Gráinne.

DONN
Lord of Death; places of residence included Knock Fierna, off Béara, the southwest coast of Kerry, and Doonbeg in Clare.

DONN OF COOLEY
The great Brown Bull; cause of the *Táin Bó Cuailnge.*

DUAIBHSEACH
Wife of Muircheartach Mac Erca.

ECHDAE
Sky god associated with horses; one of Áine's husbands.

EIBHLIU
Lover of Eochaidh Mac Maireadha, with whom she fled to the place where Lough Neagh later formed.

EICHE
Virgin saint, sister of St. Mel and associated with Ardagh.

ÉIRE, ERIU
One of the three sovereign sister goddesses of the land of Ireland.

EITHNE
Wife of Conn of the Thousand Battles.

EITHNE, DAUGHTER OF CATHAOIR MÓR
Wife of Cormac Mac Airt.

ELCMAR
One of the Tuatha Dé Danann, the foster-father of Aonghus Óg.

EOCHAIDH
Horse god, husband of Áine.

EOCHAIDH ÁIREAMH
High king of Ireland; husband of the first Étaín.

EOCHAIDH MAC MAIREADHA
Lover of Eibhliu, with whom he fled to the place where Lough Neagh later formed.

EOGABEL
God and father of the goddess Áine, killed by the druid Fearcheas.

EOGHAN
Fifth-century king, baptised by St. Patrick.

EOGHAN MAC DURTHACHT
Warrior of the Red Branch and slayer of Naoise.

EORANN
Wife of Suibhne.

ÉTAÍN, ÉADAOIN, AIDEEN
(1) Wife of Midhir, then through various transformations, wife of Eochaidh Aireamh; (2) Her daughter, daughter and wife of Eochaidh Aireamh; (3) Mes Buachalla, the cowherd's fosterling—daughter and granddaughter of Eochaidh.

ÉTAR
Father of Étaín in her mortal form and king of Echrad.

ETHAL ANBHUAIL
King of the Munster Sídh.

ETHLINN
Daughter of Balor and Ceithlenn; mother of Lugh.

FAND
Woman of the Sídh, she was the wife of Manannán and the lover of Cú Chulainn.

FAS
Milesian princess associated with the Glen Fas area of Kerry.

FEAR DORCHA
The Dark Man, the magician who enchanted Fionn's wife, Sadhbh.

FEARCHEAS
Leinster druid, he was the killer of Eogabel, the father of the goddess Áine.

FEDELM
Prophetess who foretold the slaughter of the *Táin Bó Cuailgne*.

FEIRCHEIRDNE
Cú Roí's harper.

FER FÍ
Brother of the goddess Áine.

FERDIA
Connacht champion; foster-brother of Cú Chulainn.

FERGUS MAC RÓICH
Ulster warrior, originally king of Ulster; went into exile in Connacht after Conchobhar tricked him into betraying Deirdre and the Sons of Usna; Maeve's lover.

FIACHRA
One of the Children of Lir.

FINIAN THE LEPER
Seventh-century saint, credited with founding Inisfallen Abbey in Killarney.

FINNBHEANNACH
The White-Horn—Ailill's great bull.

FINTAN, FIONNTAN MAC BÓCHNA
The oldest man—the seer who lived from the time of the first invasion of Ireland.

FINVARRA
In Connacht folklore—the king of the fairies who has his home at Knockma.

FIONN
Champion, hunter, hero; leader of the Fianna hunting troop.

FIONNABHAIR
Daughter of Maeve; promised to the Connacht champions as a reward for fighting Cú Chulainn.

FIONNUALA
One of the Children of Lir, changed into a swan by Aoife.

FIR BOLG
Descendants of the Nemedians, they were defeated by the Tuatha Dé Danann at the First Battle of Moytura but later returned to Ireland when they held fortresses on the western shoreline; they were finally defeated by King Cairbre.

FLIODHAS
Guardian of wild creatures, particularly deer; sometimes said to be the wife of Fergus Mac Róich and the mother of Lí Ban.

FÓDHLA
One of the three sister goddesses of sovereignty of Ireland.

FOMORIANS (FOMHÓIRE)
Race of malevolent beings who oppressed the Tuatha Dé Danann until eventually defeated by them at the Second Battle of Moytura.

FOTHADH CANAINNE
Mythical warrior and husband of the Hag of Béara.

FRIGUAN
Legendary builder of the Grianán of Aileach.

FUAMNACH
First wife of Midhir; enchantress who transformed Étaín.

GAIBHLEANN GABHA
Mythical smith said to live on the Béara peninsula.

GOIBHNIU
God of smithcraft—he forged magical weapons for the Tuatha Dé Danann at the second battle of Moytura.

GOLL MAC MORNA
One of the Fianna; killed by Fionn.

GRÁINNE
Daughter of Cormac Mac Airt; wife of Diarmuid and later of Fionn.

HAG OF BÉARA
In Irish, the *Cailleach Bhéarra*; appears in various forms throughout Ireland; often associated with harvest time and with creating physical features in the landscape.

HAWK OF ACHILL
Mythological bird to whom the seer Fintan told his story.

INCGEL
British sea-pirate whose warriors killed Conaire, son of Étaín.

IORNACH
One of the three Hags of Keshcorann.

IUCHAR
King of the Isle of Man; father of Bláthnaid.

LABHRAIDH
Druidic sorcerer, father of Fintan.

LAEG
Cú Chulainn's charioteer.

LAOGHAIRE
Son of Niall of the Nine Hostages and high king, converted to Christianity by St. Patrick after many years of opposition to the saint.

LEABHARCHAM
Female satirist and poet; nurse of Deirdre.

LÍ BAN
Princess transformed into a mermaid after the flooding of Lough Neagh.

LIR
One of the Tuatha Dé Danann, he lived at his *sídh* in Armagh; he was the father of children changed into swans by the enchantress Aoife.

LOINGSEACHÁN
Friend and helper of Suibhne.

LON MAC LÍOMTHA
Magical three-armed smith; lived in Keshcorann caves.

LUCHRA
Enchantress who, out of jealousy, turned Aife into a crane.

LUGH, LÁMHFHADA, LUGH OF THE LONG ARM
The many-skilled god, adept at all crafts and skills of battle; god of light and sun, celebrated at Lughnasa, the time of harvest; killer of his grandfather, Balor, at the Battle of Moytura, and later king over all the Tuatha Dé Danann.

MAC CÉCHT
One of the Tuatha Dé Danann; master-healer.

MAC ROTH
Messenger of Maeve of Connacht.

MACHA
Goddess of pastures, horses, fertility, kingship and, in one form, of battle; often known as Macha the Red.

MAEVE, MEADBH, MEDB
Queen of Connacht; main instigator of the *Táin Bó Cuailgne.*

MAIRIDH
King of Munster and father of Eochaidh; Eochaidh fled with his wife.

MANANNÁN MAC LIR
Deity of the oceans, and the magical otherworld, the Many-Coloured Land; in his human form, said to be buried in Lough Corrib.

MEL
Fifth-century saint and bishop, associated with Ardagh.

MES BUACHALLA
The third Étaín, mother of King Conaire.

MIDHIR
One of the Tuatha Dé Danann; lover of Étaín and dweller in Brí Léith.

MÍL
Leader of the last invasion of Ireland, when the Milesians defeated the Tuatha Dé Danann and sent them into the hollow hills.

MILESIANS, SONS OF MÍL
Last invaders of Ireland; the tribe who defeated the Tuatha Dé Danann.

MIS
Princess who went mad when her father was killed; was restored by the power of music; the Slieve Mish mountains in Kerry are called after her.

MOCHAOMHÓG
Hermit on Inis Glora who buried the Children of Lir.

MOLING
Saint and hermit; lover of nature and protector of Suibhne in his last days.

MONGAN
Son of Manannán Mac Lir and famous shape-shifter and magician.

MONGÁN
Moling's cowherd; killer of Suibhne.

MORGAN
Father of Dealbhchaem, killed by Art.

MORRIGAN
War goddess, one of the triple battle furies; said to come from the cave of Owneygat at Cruachan at Samhain, the feast of the dead at the beginning of November.

MUIRCHEARTACH MAC ERCA
High king of Ireland in the sixth century; loved by Sín who also killed him.

MUIRGIL
Wife of Moling's cowherd, Mongán.

NAOISE
Eldest of the Sons of Usna; lover of Deirdre; killed by Conchobhar.

NEMED, NEIMHEADH
Leader of the Nemedians; one of the husbands of Macha.

NEMEDIANS
The people of Nemed, the third tribe to invade Ireland; defeated by the Fomorion giants but the remnants of the tribe escaped and fled to the northern islands and to Greece.

NERA
Hero of the court of Maeve, who visited the Otherworld and married a woman of the Sídh.

NIAMH
Princess of the Otherworld; lover of Oisín.

NUADHU
God of the Tuatha Dé Danann; gave up kingship after he lost his arm at the First Battle of Moytura; known as Nuadhu of the Silver Arm.

OGMA
One of the Tuatha Dé Danann; credited with giving his name to ogham script, the most ancient form of writing in Ireland.

OISÍN
Son of Fionn and Sadhbh; lover of Niamh; returned to Ireland after 300 years in the Land of Youth and met St. Patrick.

OSCAR
Son of Oisín; traditionally said to have been killed at the Battle of Gabhra, the Fianna's last and major defeat.

PARTHALON
Leader of the second invasion of Ireland; his people lived in Ireland until destroyed in a great plague.

PATRICK
Patron saint of Ireland, credited with introducing Christianity to the country in the fifth century AD.

RED BRANCH WARRIORS
See Craobh Rua.

RÓNÁN
Seventh-century king who slew his own son in a jealous rage.

ROS MAC DEADHA
Warrior sent by King Cairbre against the Fir Bolg.

SADHBH
Woman of the Sídh, wife of Fionn; mother of Oisín.

SCEOLAN
Fionn's hound.

SCOTA
Mythical queen of the Milesians.

SGANNLACH
Daughter of Fionn and wife of Goll Mac Morna.

SÍDH (PERSON)
Otherwordly, ever-young being with magical powers; mainly the later transformation of the Tuatha Dé Danann.

SÍDH (PLACE)
The mounds where the Sídh lived.

SIGE
King, father of Sín, killed by Muircheartach Mac Erca.

SÍN
Enchantress; lover and murderer of Muircheartach Mac Erca.

SUIBHNE
King of Dál Riada in Ulster; went mad at the Battle of Moira and spent the rest of his life in the trees until killed by a jealous cowherd.

TAILTIU
Foster-mother of Lugh, who instigated the Tailtiu games in her honour.

TORDRE
Retainer and spy of Conchobhar Mac Neasa.

TUATHA DÉ DANANN
Otherworld conquerors of Ireland; defeated the Fir Bolg and the Fomorians and ruled Ireland until they themselves were defeated by the Milesians; took refuge in the world of hollow mounds and in magical islands far out to sea, but often used their otherworldly powers to help or hinder mortals; later became known as the Sídh.

UAINIDHE
Mythological figure associated with Áine and commemorated on Knockainey Hill.

UILEANN RED EDGE
Mythical figure associated with Lough Corrib, the killer of Manannán Mac Lir.

USNA, SONS OF
The eldest of these three, Naoise, was the lover of Deirdre; the three brothers fled to Scotland with her until tricked into returning to Ireland where they were killed by Conchobar Mac Neasa.

Glossary of Archaeological Terms

Bronze Age *c.* 2000BC–300BC
The period when metal-working in bronze and gold was introduced to Ireland until the time of the introduction of iron.

Cairn
Large mound often covering a prehistoric burial structure.

Cashel (*caiseal*), cathair
Stone-built circular enclosures. These are the stone versions of the ringforts which were the dwelling-places of the farming population during the early Christian period, although some of them may have their origins in the Iron Age. These terms are often incorporated into place-names (*See* ringforts).

Celts
Generic term covering the tribes which had their origin in central Europe *c.*1200BC. The strongest surviving elements of their culture and language are on the western seaboard, including

Brittany, Scotland, Wales, Cornwall and, most particularly, Ireland.

Crannóg

A man-made island deliberately situated in the centre of a lake for the purposes of defence. The earliest examples date from the late Bronze Age and many continued in use up to the Middle Ages.

Cromlech

A portal tomb.

Dolmen

Term used to describe the remains of Megalithic tombs, consisting of a large flat stone laid on two uprights.

Dún

General term used to describe a dwelling in the ancient texts, usually with connotation of prestige and fortification.

Forts

Hill-forts:

Enormous circular enclosures, believed to have been used for the purposes of defence and, more especially, as tribal assembly places. There are about fifty of these in the country and they are usually placed on prominent sites in the landscape. It is now known that they had their origins in the late Bronze Age although they continued in use for a long time after that. Well-known examples are Dún Aonghusa and Dún Chonchobhair on the Aran Islands and Rathgall in County Wicklow.

Promontory Forts:

There are about 250 coastal promontory forts around Ireland, where a sea-girt promontory is defended on the land-side by banks of earth and stone. Inland promontory forts, which number fewer than a dozen, are in spectacular locations on the edge of mountain tops. A good example of the latter is Caherconree in County Kerry.

Grianán

Term used to describe a sun-palace.

Iron Age

c. 500BC to *c.* 500AD—the period when iron began to be used in Ireland.

Megalithic

General term used to describe prehistoric stone monuments.

Megalithic Tombs

Term used to describe prehistoric tombs built of massive stones. (Megalithic is from Greek *megas*—"great, large" and *lithos*—"stone"). Mostly built in the Neolithic period (New Stone Age) by the early farming population. Over 1,450 Megalithic tombs have been recorded in Ireland and they are classified into four types:

Court Tombs:

These have an open court leading to the burial area which consists of two or more chambers under a stone and earthen cairn. They have mostly a northern distribution. Creevykeel in County Sligo is one important site of this type of tomb.

Portal Dolmens:

The word dolmen, like cromlech, was formerly used for Megalithic tombs in general. The word comes from Breton *taol* (table), and *maen* (stone). The term is more often restricted to portal tombs today. There are 174 portal tombs in Ireland and they are spectacular monuments such as Poulnabrone in the Burren in County Clare. A large, flat capstone rests upon upright stones. These monuments are often known as *Leaba Dhiarmada agus Gráinne* in local lore as tradition has it that they were the resting places of the famous lovers during their flight from Fionn.

Passage Tombs:

There are 230 passage tombs in Ireland, each consisting of a narrow passage leading to a large chamber. They often have corbelled roofs under a cairn and carvings on the structural stones. The best and most famous collection of Megalithic art in Europe is found in the great tombs of the *Brú na Bóinne*, or Bend of the Boyne, complex in County Meath.

Wedge Tombs:

These are believed to be the latest type of Megalithic tomb. They consist of a rectangular chamber inside a cairn and are associated with Bronze Age activity. They are found mainly in the southwest of the country.

Mesolithic

Middle Stone Age—covering *c.* 7500BC to *c.* 3500BC. Pre-farming, hunter-gatherer stage of civilisation.

Neolithic

New Stone Age covering the period from the introduction of farming to the introduction of metal-working—*c.* 3500BC to *c.* 2000BC.

Ogham Stone

Upright stone carved with ogham script, usually the name and genealogy of an individual. The script dates from 300AD onwards.

Palaeolithic

Old Stone Age—the period directly after the Ice Age *c.* 18000BC to *c.* 7500BC. No evidence of life in Ireland.

Pillarstone

Upright stone, sometimes part of a stone circle.

Ring-barrow

General term for a circular tumulus.

Ringfort

A circular enclosure of earth or stone, the ringfort is the most frequently encountered field monument in Ireland. Ringforts number about 50,000 and are known by various names—cashel (*caiseal*) and cathair for the stone versions, *rath*, *lios* and *dún* in earthen form. They were the farmsteads, sometimes fortified, of the Irish population from the Iron Age onwards. Many of them were still occupied up to medieval times.

Map of Sites

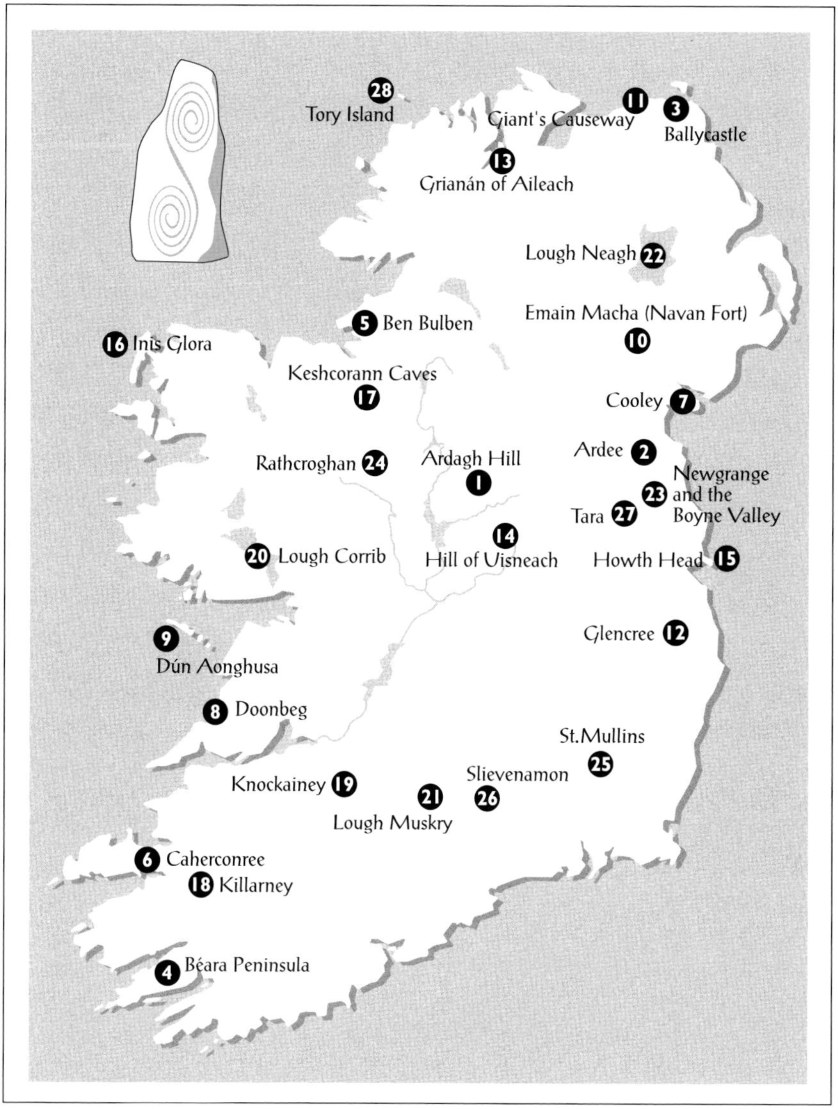

Map Key

(See ***Direction Key*** *for further information on how to locate the sites)*

1. Ardagh Hill, Longford
2. Ardee, Louth
3. Ballycastle, Antrim
4. Béara Peninsula, Cork
5. Ben Bulben, Sligo
6. Caherconree, Kerry
7. Cooley, Louth
8. Doonbeg, Clare
9. Dún Aonghusa, Inishmore, Galway
10. Emain Macha (Navan Fort), Armagh
11. Giant's Causeway, Antrim
12. Glencree
13. Grianán of Aileach, Donegal
14. Hill of Uisneach, Westmeath
15. Howth Head, Dublin
16. Inis Glora, Mayo
17. Keshcorann Caves, Sligo
18. Killarney, Kerry
19. Knockainey, Limerick
20. Lough Corrib, Galway
21. Lough Muskry, Tipperary
22. Lough Neagh, Antrim
23. Newgrange, Meath
24. Rathcroghan, Roscommon
25. St. Mullins, Carlow
26. Slievenamon, Tipperary
27. Tara, Meath
28. Tory Island, Donegal

Direction Key

A note on access

Up until quite recently, access through private land to sites of historic or scenic interest was not a problem in Ireland. This has now changed in some areas. For the sake of politeness, it is always better to request access if your route to a site leads you through private land.

Ardagh Hill, Longford

Situated just off the R393 between Mullingar and Longford. The hill is to the west of the village and it is possible to drive around it.

Ardee, Louth

Ardee is about 65 kilometres (40 miles) from Dublin on the N2 between Slane and Carrickmacross. The ford is to the left of the bridge leading into the town from the Slane side. There is parking to the left just over the bridge.

Ballycastle, Antrim

Ballycastle is situated on the extreme northeastern point of Ulster. Pan's Rocks are located on the western end of Ballycastle beach, just under Fair Head.

Béara Peninsula, Cork

The "Ring of Béara" is well signposted from Glengarrif on the south and Kenmare on the north.

Ben Bulben, Sligo

The North Ben Bulben plateau can be reached from a starting point at Glenade Lough, on a branch road from the R280 between Kinlough and Manorhamilton. For up-to-date information on access, ask at the Tourist Office in Sligo town.

Caherconree, Kerry

Take the R561 west from Castlemaine and the right turn from Aughil's Bridge towards Camp. The route up the mountain is to your right.

Cooley, Louth

The peninsula is situated just to the north of Dundalk. Follow the signs from Dundalk after taking the N1 to leave the town. The Táin Trail is signposted at various points along the road which runs around the peninsula.

Doonbeg, Clare

Situated on the N67, about 10 kilometres (6 miles) north of Kilkee. Numerous small roads lead westwards into the dunes.

Dún Aonghusa, Inishmore, Galway

There are regular ferries to Inishmore from Rossaveal, west of Galway city, and there is also a flight service from the city by Aer Árainn. Dún Aonghusa is about a kilometre (half a mile) from the harbour on Inishmore.

Emain Macha (Navan Fort), Armagh
Take the A28 west from Armagh city; the fort is less than 2 kilometres (1.25 miles) away. The interpretative centre was closed during the summer of 2002.

Giant's Causeway, Antrim
Located between Bushmills and Dunseverick on the A2. Well-signposted.

Glencree
Take the minor road to the southwest of Enniskerry towards Lough Bray. It is possible to do a circuit of the glen and Knockree by car. Glencree can also be reached from the west, via the R115.

Grianán of Aileach, Donegal
West of Derry city on the N13 heading towards Letterkenny. It is signposted from the N13, and the access road to the Grianán is just beside the interpretative centre—a converted church.

Hill of Uisneach, Westmeath
From Mullingar, take the R390 towards Athlone. About 8 kilometres (5 miles) before Ballymore, it is signposted. The Catstone is signposted from the same road a little further on.

Howth Head, Dublin
Howth Head is just under 16 kilometres (10 miles) from Dublin city centre. Follow the R105 northwards along the coast. The Deerpark Hotel, site of Aideen's Tomb, is signposted from the road just before you reach Howth village, and the cliff walk to the promontory fort and the Baily Lighthouse is signposted from Howth Summit car park.

Inis Glora, Erris Peninsula, Mayo
You can travel to Belmullet by taking either the R313 from Bangor or the R314 from Ballycastle, both in the extreme north of Mayo. Inis Glora has no regular ferry service so ask locally to arrange travel to the islands. Geraghtys (097-85741) and Lavelles (097-85669) organise charters.

Keshcorann Caves, Sligo
Take the R295 from Boyle to Ballymote. There is an access road to the nearest point to the caves just after the village of Keash on the right-hand side. The route to the cave leads through private land.

Killarney, Kerry
The lakes are situated to the southwest of the town, well signposted on the N71.

Knockainey, Limerick
Take the R516 from Hospital to Bruff. The road to Knockainey is signposted to the right.

Lough Corrib, Galway
Annaghdoon is situated on the eastern shore of the lake off the N84. Cong is on the northern tip on the R346, and Clonbur is a little to the west.

Lough Muskry, Tipperary
The Glen of Aherlow is signposted to the south from Tipperary town. The village of Rossadrehid on the south side of the glen is the best starting point for the walk. The walk is signposted from the village and the return journey should take no more than three hours in total.

Lough Neagh, Antrim
Ardboe is situated just off the B73, on the west coast of the lough, not far east of Cookstown.

Newgrange and the Boyne Valley, Meath
The Brú na Bóinne complex lies between Slane and Drogheda. It is approximately 56 kilometres (35 miles) north of Dublin and is signposted from the N2. Rosnaree House is on the south bank of the Boyne on a minor road. Stackallen Bridge is on the Navan–Slane Road, and Ardmulchan Church is signposted off the minor Navan–Slane Road which runs south of the river.

Rathcroghan, Roscommon
Situated between Tulsk and Frenchpark on the N5. Well signposted.

St. Mullins, Carlow
Just off the R729 to the south of Glynn village between Borris and New Ross. Signposted.

Slievenamon, Tipperary
Kilcash is situated on the N76 between Kilkenny and Clonmel. Follow the signposts for the Slievenamon Drive.

Tara, Meath
Tara is signposted to the left of the N3 between Dublin and Navan. It is approximately 48 kilometres (30 miles) north of Dublin.

Tory Island, Donegal
A regular ferry service runs to Tory from Bunbeg and Magheroarty—the second is the much shorter route. Magheroarty is west of Gortahork on the R257. The ferry is very much influenced by weather conditions.

Bibliography

THE STORIES

Direct Translations

Dooley, Ann, and Harry Roe (translators), *Tales of the Elders of Ireland*, Oxford University Press, Oxford, 1999.

Gwynn, Edward, *The Metrical Dindshenchas*, Royal Irish Academy, Dublin, 1905.

MacAlister, RA Stewart (ed. and translator), *Lebor Gabála Érenn; The Book of the Taking of Ireland*, Pts 1–5, Irish Texts Society, Dublin, 1938.

Murphy, Gerard (ed. and translator), *Duanaire Finn*, Pts. 1–3, Irish Texts Society, Dublin, 1935.

O'Grady, Standish, *Silva Gadelica*, Williams and Norgate, London, 1892.

O'Keefe, JG (ed. and translator), *The Adventures of Suibhne Geilt*, Irish Texts Society, London, 1913.

Literary Translations, Re-tellings and Studies

Arbois de Jubainville, Henri, *The Irish Mythological Cycle and Celtic Mythology*, Hodges Figgis, Dublin, 1903.

Bitel, Lisa M., *Land of Women; Tales of Sex and Gender*, Cornell University Press, Ithaca, NY, 1996.

Cross, Tom Peete, and Clark Harris Slover, *Ancient Irish Tales*, Barnes and Noble, New York, 1996.

Curran, Bob, *Complete Guide to Celtic Mythology*, Appletree Press, Belfast, 2000.

Dillon, Myles, *Irish Sagas*, Stationery Office, Dublin, 1959.

Dixon-Kennedy, Mike, *Celtic Myth and Legend—An A–Z of People and Places*, Blandford, London, 1996.

Gantz, Jeffrey, *Early Irish Myths and Sagas*, Penguin, London, 1981.

Green, Miranda, *A Dictionary of Celtic Myth and Legend*, Thames and Hudson, London, 1992.

Gregory, Augusta, *Lady Gregory's Complete Irish Mythology*, Smithmark, London, 2000.

Harpur, Patrick, *The Philosopher's Secret Fire—A History of the Imagination*, Penguin, London, 2002.

Heaney, Marie, *Over Nine Waves*, Faber and Faber, London, 1994.

Heaney, Seamus, *Sweeney Astray*, Faber and Faber, London, 1984.

Jackson, Kenneth, *A Celtic Miscellany*, Routledge and Kegan Paul, London, 1951.

Joyce, PW, *Old Celtic Romances*, David Nutt, London, 1879.

Kane, Sean, *Wisdom of the Mythtellers*, Broadview Press, Peterborough, Ontario, 1994.

Kinsella, Thomas, *The Táin*, Dolmen Press, Dublin, 1969.
Mac Cana, Prionsias, *Celtic Mythology*, Hamlyn, London, 1970.
Mallory, JP (ed.), *Aspects of the Táin*, December Publications, Belfast, 1992.
Meyer, Kuno, *The Death Tales of the Ulster Heroes*, Royal Irish Academy, Dublin, 1906.
Muller-Lisowski, Kate, 'Contributions to a Study of Irish Folklore: Traditions about Donn', *Béaloideas* 18, pp. 142–99.
Murphy, Gerald, *Saga and Myth in Ancient Ireland,* At the Sign of the Three Candles, Dublin, 1961.
Ó hÓgáin, Dáithí, *Myth, Legend and Romance*, Ryan Publishers, London, 1990.
Ó hÓgáin, Dáithí, *Fionn Mac Cumhaill*, Gill and Macmillan, Dublin, 1988.
Ó hÓgáin, Dáithí, *The Sacred Isle: Belief and Religion in Pre-Christian Ireland*, Collins Press, Cork, 1999.
O'Rahilly, Thomas, *Early Irish History and Mythology*, Dublin Institute for Advanced Studies, Dublin, 1946.
Rees, Alwyn and Brinley, *Celtic Heritage*, Thames and Hudson, London, 1991.
Rolleston, TW, *Myths and Legends of the Celtic Race*, George C. Harrap, London, 1911.
Sjoestedt, Marie Louise, *Gods and Heroes of the Celts* (trans. Myles Dillon), Turtle Island Foundation, Berkeley, 1982.
Smyth, Daragh, *A Guide to Irish Mythology*, Irish Academic Press, Dublin, 1988.
Stephens, James, *In the Land of Youth*, Macmillan, New York, 1924.
Stephens, James, *Irish Fairy Tales*, Gill and Macmillan, Dublin, 1995.
Wilde, Lady, *Ancient Legends of Ireland*, Poolbeg, Dublin, 2000.

THE SITES

Automobile Association, *Illustrated Road Book of Ireland*, Automobile Association, Dublin, 1966.
Bourke, Angela, *The Burning of Bridget Cleary*, Pimlico, London, 1999.
Brennan, JH, *A Guide to Megalithic Ireland*, Aquarian Press, London,1994.
Brenneman, Walter L., *Crossing the Circle at the Holy Wells of Ireland*, University Press of Virginia, Charlottesville, 1995.
Buckley, Victor, *The Archaeological Inventory of County Louth*, The Stationery Office, Dublin, 1986.
Cunningham, Noreen, and Pat McGinn, *The Gap of the North*, The O'Brien Press, Dublin, 2001.
Cuppage, Judith (ed.), *Archaeological Survey of the Dingle Peninsula*, Oidhreacht Chorca Dhuibhne, Ballyferriter, 1986.
Dames, Michael, *Ireland, a Sacred Journey*, Element Books, Shaftesbury, 2000.
Dames, Michael, *Mythic Ireland*, Thames and Hudson, London, 1992.
Devlin, Polly, *The Far Side of the Lough*, Gollancz, London, 1993.
Donnelly, Maureen, *The Nine Glens*, Donard Press, Bangor, 1977.
Durrell, Penelope, *Discover Dursey*, Ballinancarriga Books, Allihies, 1996.

Eogan, George, *Knowth and the Passage Tombs of Ireland*, Thames and Hudson, New York, 1986.

Evans, E. Estyn, *Prehistoric and Early Christian Ireland*, Batsford, London, 1966.

Flanagan, Laurence, *A Dictionary of Irish Archaeology*, Gill and Macmillan, Dublin, 1992.

Flanagan, Laurence, *Ancient Ireland; Life before the Celts*, Gill and Macmillan, Dublin, 1998.

Fox, Robin, *The Tory Islanders—a People on the Celtic Fringe*, Cambridge University Press, Cambridge, 1978.

Green, Miranda, *The Celtic World*, Routledge, London, 1995.

Hannigan, Ken, and William Nolan, *Wicklow, History and Society*, Geography Publications, Dublin, 1994.

Harbison, Peter, *Pre-Christian Ireland: from the First Settlers to the Early Celts*, Thames and Hudson, London, 1988.

Healy, Elizabeth, *Literary Tour of Ireland*, Wolfhound Press, Dublin, 1995.

Herity, Michael, *Rathcroghan and Carnfree—Celtic Royal Sites of Roscommon*, Na Clocha Breaca, Dublin, 1988.

Hickey, Elizabeth, 'The House of Cletty', *Ríocht na Midhe*, Vol. iii, No. 3, 1965, pp. 181–6.

Higgins, Jim, *Corrib County Archaeology*, Corrib Conservation Centre, Galway, 1991.

Kennedy, Gerald, *Irish Mythology, visiting the places*, Morrigan, Killala, 1993.

Kockel, Ulrich (ed.), *Landscape, Heritage and Identity*, Liverpool University Press, Liverpool, 1995.

Lacey, Brian, *The Archaeological Survey of Donegal*, Donegal County Council, Lifford, 1983.

Le Fanu, William, *Seventy Years of Irish Life*, Arnold, London, 1928.

Logan, Patrick, *The Holy Wells of Ireland,* Colin Smythe, Buckinghamshire, 1980.

McDonagh, Steve, *The Dingle Peninsula: History, Folklore, Archaeology,* Brandon, Dingle, 1993.

Mac Neill, Máire, *The Festival of Lughnasa*, Oxford University Press, Oxford, 1962.

Meehan, Cary, *A Traveller's Guide to Sacred Ireland*, Gothic Image, Glastonbury, 2002.

Morris, Henry, 'Where was Bruidhean Dá Derga?' *Journal of the Royal Society of Antiquaries of Ireland*, 1935, pp. 297–312.

Ó hÉithir, Breandán, *An Aran Reader*, Lilliput Press, Dublin 1991.

O'Doherty, John, *Aileach of the Kings*, Catholic Truth Society of Ireland, Dublin, 1908.

O'Donovan, John, *The Antiquities of County Clare*, Clasp Press, Ennis, 1997.

O'Flanagan, Michael, *Letters containing information relevant to the antiquities of Meath*, M. O'Flanagan, Bray, 1928.

O'Kelly, Michael J., *Early Ireland: an Introduction to Irish Pre-history*, Cambridge University Press, Cambridge, 1989.

O'Kelly, Michael, *Newgrange: Archaeology, Art and Legends*, Thames and Hudson, London, 1982.

Ó Ríordáin, Seán P., *Antiquities of the Irish Countryside*. Revised by Ruaidhrí de Valera, Routledge, London, 1979.
O'Sullivan, Muiris et al., *Archaeological Features at Risk*, The Heritage Council, Kilkenny, 2000.
O'Sullivan, Ted, *Bere Island*, Inisgragy Books, Cork, 1992.
Raftery, Barry, *Pagan Celtic Ireland: The Enigma of the Irish Iron Age*, Thames and Hudson, London, 1994.
Robinson, Tim, *Stones of Aran: Labyrinth,* Lilliput Press, Dublin, 1995.
Robinson, Tim, *Stones of Aran: Pilgrimage*, Lilliput Press, Dublin, 1986.
Slavin, Michael, *The Book of Tara*, Wolfhound Press, Dublin, 1996.
Smyth, Daragh, and Gerry Kennedy, *Places of Mythology in Ireland*, Morrigan, Killala, 1989.
Swan, Harry P., *Romantic Stories and Legends of Donegal*, WJ Barr, Letterkenny, 1969.
Taylor, Lawrence J., *Occasions of Faith: an Anthropology of Irish Catholics*, Lilliput Press, Dublin, 1995.
Watson, Philip, *The Giant's Causeway,* The O'Brien Press, Dublin, 2000.
Westropp, Thomas J., *Folklore of County Clare*, Clasp Press, Ennis, 2000.
Wilde, Sir William, *The Beauties of the Boyne and its tributary the Blackwater*, James McGlashan, Dublin, 1849.
Wilde, Sir William, *Lough Corrib, its Shores and Islands*, McGlashan and Gill, Dublin, 1872.